OFFICIAL SQA PAST PAPERS WITH ANSWERS

INTERMEDIATE 2

BIOLOGY
2009-2013

Hodder Gibson Study Skills Advice – General — page 3
Hodder Gibson Study Skills Advice – Intermediate 2 Biology — page 5
2009 EXAM — page 7
2010 EXAM — page 43
2011 EXAM — page 75
2012 EXAM — page 107
2013 EXAM — page 139
ANSWER SECTION — page 171

Hodder Gibson is grateful to the copyright holders, as credited on the final page of the Question Section, for permission to use their material. Every effort has been made to trace the copyright holders and to obtain their permission for the use of copyright material. Hodder Gibson will be happy to receive information allowing us to rectify any error or omission in future editions.

Hachette UK's policy is to use papers that are natural, renewable and recyclable products and made from wood grown in sustainable forests. The logging and manufacturing processes are expected to conform to the environmental regulations of the country of origin.

Orders: please contact Bookpoint Ltd, 130 Park Drive, Abingdon, Oxon OX14 4SE. Telephone: (44) 01235 827720. Fax: (44) 01235 400454.

Lines are open 9.00–5.00, Monday to Saturday, with a 24-hour message answering service. Visit our website at www.hoddereducation.co.uk. Hodder Gibson can be contacted direct on: Tel: 0141 848 1609; Fax: 0141 889 6315; email: hoddergibson@hodder.co.uk

This collection first published in 2013 by

Hodder Gibson, an imprint of Hodder Education,

An Hachette UK Company

2a Christie Street

Paisley PA1 1NB

BrightRED PUBLISHING   Hodder Gibson is grateful to Bright Red Publishing Ltd for collaborative work in preparation of this book and all SQA Past Paper and National 5 Model Paper titles 2013.

Typeset by PDQ Digital Media Solutions Ltd, Bungay, Suffolk NR35 1BY

Printed in the UK

A catalogue record for this title is available from the British Library

ISBN 978-1-4718-0243-0

3 2 1

2014 2013

Introduction

Study Skills – what you need to know to pass exams!

Pause for thought

Many students might skip quickly through a page like this. After all, we all know how to revise. Do you really though?

Think about this:

"IF YOU ALWAYS DO WHAT YOU ALWAYS DO, YOU WILL ALWAYS GET WHAT YOU HAVE ALWAYS GOT."

Do you like the grades you get? Do you want to do better? If you get full marks in your assessment, then that's great! Change nothing! This section is just to help you get that little bit better than you already are.

There are two main parts to the advice on offer here. The first part highlights fairly obvious things but which are also very important. The second part makes suggestions about revision that you might not have thought about but which WILL help you.

Part 1

DOH! It's so obvious but …

Start revising in good time

Don't leave it until the last minute – this will make you panic.

Make a revision timetable that sets out work time AND play time.

Sleep and eat!

Obvious really, and very helpful. Avoid arguments or stressful things too – even games that wind you up. You need to be fit, awake and focused!

Know your place!

Make sure you know exactly **WHEN and WHERE** your exams are.

Know your enemy!

Make sure you know what to expect in the exam.

How is the paper structured?

How much time is there for each question?

What types of question are involved?

Which topics seem to come up time and time again?

Which topics are your strongest and which are your weakest?

Are all topics compulsory or are there choices?

Learn by DOING!

There is no substitute for past papers and practice papers – they are simply essential! Tackling this collection of papers and answers is exactly the right thing to be doing as your exams approach.

Part 2

People learn in different ways. Some like low light, some bright. Some like early morning, some like evening / night. Some prefer warm, some prefer cold. But everyone uses their BRAIN and the brain works when it is active. Passive learning – sitting gazing at notes – is the most INEFFICIENT way to learn anything. Below you will find tips and ideas for making your revision more effective and maybe even more enjoyable. What follows gets your brain active, and active learning works!

Activity 1 – Stop and review

Step 1

When you have done no more than 5 minutes of revision reading STOP!

Step 2

Write a heading in your own words which sums up the topic you have been revising.

Step 3

Write a summary of what you have revised in no more than two sentences. Don't fool yourself by saying, 'I know it but I cannot put it into words'. That just means you don't know it well enough. If you cannot write your summary, revise that section again, knowing that you must write a summary at the end of it. Many of you will have notebooks full of blue/black ink writing. Many of the pages will not be especially attractive or memorable so try to liven them up a bit with colour as you are reviewing and rewriting. **This is a great memory aid, and memory is the most important thing.**

Activity 2 — Use technology!

Why should everything be written down? Have you thought about 'mental' maps, diagrams, cartoons and colour to help you learn? And rather than write down notes, why not record your revision material?

What about having a text message revision session with friends? Keep in touch with them to find out how and what they are revising and share ideas and questions.

Why not make a video diary where you tell the camera what you are doing, what you think you have learned and what you still have to do? No one has to see or hear it but the process of having to organise your thoughts in a formal way to explain something is a very important learning practice.

Be sure to make use of electronic files. You could begin to summarise your class notes. Your typing might be slow but it will get faster and the typed notes will be easier to read than the scribbles in your class notes. Try to add different fonts and colours to make your work stand out. You can easily Google relevant pictures, cartoons and diagrams which you can copy and paste to make your work more attractive and **MEMORABLE**.

Activity 3 – This is it. Do this and you will know lots!

Step 1

In this task you must be very honest with yourself! Find the SQA syllabus for your subject (www.sqa.org.uk). Look at how it is broken down into main topics called MANDATORY knowledge. That means stuff you MUST know.

Step 2

BEFORE you do ANY revision on this topic, write a list of everything that you already know about the subject. It might be quite a long list but you only need to write it once. It shows you all the information that is already in your long-term memory so you know what parts you do not need to revise!

Step 3

Pick a chapter or section from your book or revision notes. Choose a fairly large section or a whole chapter to get the most out of this activity.

With a buddy, use Skype, Facetime, Twitter or any other communication you have, to play the game "If this is the answer, what is the question?". For example, if you are revising Geography and the answer you provide is "meander", your buddy would have to make up a question like "What is the word that describes a feature of a river where it flows slowly and bends often from side to side?".

Make up 10 "answers" based on the content of the chapter or section you are using. Give this to your buddy to solve while you solve theirs.

Step 4

Construct a wordsearch of at least 10 X 10 squares. You can make it as big as you like but keep it realistic. Work together with a group of friends. Many apps allow you to make wordsearch puzzles online. The words and phrases can go in any direction and phrases can be split. Your puzzle must only contain facts linked to the topic you are revising. Your task is to find 10 bits of information to hide in your puzzle but you must not repeat information that you used in Step 3. DO NOT show where the words are. Fill up empty squares with random letters. Remember to keep a note of where your answers are hidden but do not show your friends. When you have a complete puzzle, exchange it with a friend to solve each other's puzzle.

Step 5

Now make up 10 questions (not "answers" this time) based on the same chapter used in the previous two tasks. Again, you must find NEW information that you have not yet used. Now it's getting hard to find that new information! Again, give your questions to a friend to answer.

Step 6

As you have been doing the puzzles, your brain has been actively searching for new information. Now write a NEW LIST that contains only the new information you have discovered when doing the puzzles. Your new list is the one to look at repeatedly for short bursts over the next few days. Try to remember more and more of it without looking at it. After a few days, you should be able to add words from your second list to your first list as you increase the information in your long-term memory.

FINALLY! Be inspired...

Make a list of different revision ideas and beside each one write **THINGS I HAVE** tried, **THINGS I WILL** try and **THINGS I MIGHT** try. Don't be scared of trying something new.

And remember – "FAIL TO PREPARE AND PREPARE TO FAIL!"

Intermediate 2 Biology

The course

The Intermediate 2 Biology course is divided into three units. Unit 1 is Living Cells which covers cell structure and function, osmosis and diffusion, enzymes, respiration and photosynthesis. Unit 2 is Environmental Biology and Genetics. This unit covers ecology (ecosystems, biodiversity), fertilisation, DNA and genetics, natural selection, selective breeding and genetic engineering. Unit 3 is Animal Physiology and covers nutrition in mammals and the alimentary system, kidney function, osmoregulation, lungs and gas exchange, the heart and blood system, the brain structure function and its role in temperature regulation.

The exam

This is a general introduction highlighting common mistakes that examiners see in examination papers and offering advice on ways to avoid these and how to use the practice papers effectively.

To get more information on the course and exam, go to www.sqa.org.uk, click on Subjects, type in Biology and select Biology Intermediate 2 from the drop down menu. You will then be able to access the Intermediate 2 Biology Arrangements documents. It is useful to read the 'Content' and 'Notes' columns to learn the key words and processes prior to your exam.

Some hints and tips

Know the correct terms and watch your time

Easy marks can be lost in the exam by not learning correct names such as blood vessels, body parts and brain function. The key names you need to learn are detailed in the Arrangements documents mentioned above. Highlight these and learn them throughout the year!

Whilst on the Biology section of the SQA website, it can also be helpful to read the External Assessment Reports for Intermediate 2 as these highlight successes and problems encountered by candidates in the exam.

Time is not likely to be an issue in the exam and you should plan on taking one minute per mark. This will leave ample time to check answers and to make sure you have left no blanks.

Read the questions and instructions carefully!

Bold type is used in questions to alert you to some important aspects to be considered. Read the questions, and the words in bold type, very carefully before attempting your answer. Be careful to read all other instructions too. Sometimes you will be asked to add an arrow or a cross to a diagram further up the page. There will not be a support line for this and many students fail to spot the instruction and will lose a mark.

You do not need to answer the questions in any particular order. However, it can be helpful to do Section A first as it will help to focus your brain on Biology. This will help later in the paper. Look through Section B questions to find one that you are confident enough to answer first of all and complete this. Then move on to other questions. Sometimes, reading Section C (the extended response questions) first allows your brain to work away quietly and gives you an edge when answering this part later.

Spelling and space

Spelling is rarely an issue – the markers will sound out a misspelled word and if it sounds right will award the mark. Only a few words need to be spelled correctly if they could be confused with other words. Examples are glycogen, glucagon and glycerol.

The exam setters will try to give you lines of sufficient length for your answer. If you find yourself running out of space (and your writing is not really big!) then you may like to reconsider what you have written.

Do not score through any answer unless you are sure you do not need it. This is especially important in Section C since, if you find yourself running out of time, it will still be marked.

Completing graphs

Easy marks can be lost when completing graphs. You may be asked to add a scale and label for either the x or y axis. Look at the table of results and use the whole heading as your label. Do not shorten it in any way. For instance, if the heading is 'Time (in minutes)' do not use 'Time (in min)' or 'Time (min)'. You will lose the mark. Your scale must be a proper scale. Do not just use the figures given in the table. For example, if you are given 0, 2, 5, 8, 12, 16 in the table, your scale could be 0, 2, 4, 6, 8, 10, 12, 14, 16. Choose an appropriate scale that uses at least 50% of the given graph paper. You will normally be told whether to plot a bar graph or a line graph. When plotting a line graph use a small dot or x to mark the plot. Once all points are plotted you should join them up (dot to dot or x to x) using a ruler.

You may be asked to use data from the table or graph to answer a question. Usually this instruction will be in **bold**. You must take figures and units from the table or graph to use in your answer. A simple trend (e.g. 'it increases and decreases') will not gain the full marks (look at 2013 Paper Section B Q12 (a)).

Correct terminology

Behaviour investigations (for example, using woodlice or maggots) occur frequently, and a common error from students is to use words such as 'like' or 'prefer' when discussing the animals' response to the conditions. A conclusion would be 'the maggots move away from the light' or 'the woodlice move towards the dark' and not 'maggots do not like the light' or 'woodlice prefer the dark'.

Investigations

There has been a good response from students when requested to suggest improvements to investigations to increase reliability. Most students now respond that repeating the experiment will improve the reliability. Less well attempted are conclusions. When you are asked to make a conclusion based on an investigation, you must return to the beginning of the question and re-read the aim of the investigation. You need to consider the aim and the results before making your conclusion.

Calculations

Generally, calculations are well attempted. However, certain calculations are considered as 'A' type questions and these require a little more care. Percentage increase or percentage decrease questions are trickier than simple increases or decreases. Work out the increase (or decrease) then divide this figure by the original value. Now multiply the answer by 100 to get the percentage. Remember that the answer can be larger than 100%. These type of calculations were poorly attempted in Papers 2010 Section B Q12 (c), 2011 Section B Q6 (b) and 2013 Section B Q3 (b).

For example, see Q3 (b) in Section B of the 2013 exam – *'Calculate the percentage decrease in catalase activity in potato when the temperature increased from 40°C to 50°C.'*

- Temperature at 40°C = 2 units
- Temperature at 50°C = 1 unit
- Decrease in temperature = 1 unit
- Percentage decrease in temperature = 1 (the decrease), divided by 2 (the original value at 40°C), multiplied by 100 (to get a percentage) = 50%.

Section C questions – extended response

Section C questions are the extended response questions (sometimes called 'essays'). They account for 10 marks (i.e. 10% of the total marks) so could be the difference between a pass and a fail. Do not leave these questions unanswered. Use bullet points if you are short of time but get the facts written down. If you have plenty time and are unsure as to which question you would get most marks from – do both! Markers will mark both answers and will award you the highest of the marks gained.

Finally, be as prepared as you can be. Use all revision aids and do as many past papers as you can get your hands on. Learn facts – you know it makes sense!

Good luck!

Remember that the rewards for passing Intermediate 2 Biology are well worth it. Your pass will help you get the future you want for yourself. In the exam, be confident in your own ability. If you're not sure how to answer a question, trust your instincts and just give it a go anyway. Keep calm and don't panic! GOOD LUCK!

[BLANK PAGE]

FOR OFFICIAL USE

Total for
Sections B and C

X007/201

NATIONAL
QUALIFICATIONS
2009

THURSDAY, 28 MAY
9.00 AM – 11.00 AM

BIOLOGY
INTERMEDIATE 2

Fill in these boxes and read what is printed below.

Full name of centre

Town

Forename(s)

Surname

Date of birth
Day Month Year

Scottish candidate number

Number of seat

SECTION A (25 marks)

Instructions for completion of Section A are given on page two.

For this section of the examination you must use an HB pencil.

SECTIONS B AND C (75 marks)

1 (a) All questions should be attempted.

(b) It should be noted that in **Section C** questions 1 and 2 each contain a choice.

2 The questions may be answered in any order but all answers are to be written in the spaces provided in this answer book, **and must be written clearly and legibly in ink**.

3 Additional space for answers will be found at the end of the book. If further space is required, supplementary sheets may be obtained from the invigilator and should be inserted inside the **front** cover of this book.

4 The numbers of questions must be clearly inserted with any answers written in the additional space.

5 Rough work, if any should be necessary, should be written in this book and then scored through when the fair copy has been written. If further space is required, a supplementary sheet for rough work may be obtained from the invigilator.

6 Before leaving the examination room you must give this book to the invigilator. If you do not, you may lose all the marks for this paper.

Read carefully

1   Check that the answer sheet provided is for **Biology Intermediate 2 (Section A)**.

2   For this section of the examination you must use an **HB pencil** and, where necessary, an eraser.

3   Check that the answer sheet you have been given has **your name**, **date of birth**, **SCN** (Scottish Candidate Number) and **Centre Name** printed on it.

     Do not change any of these details.

4   If any of this information is wrong, tell the Invigilator immediately.

5   If this information is correct, **print** your name and seat number in the boxes provided.

6   The answer to each question is **either** A, B, C or D. Decide what your answer is, then, using your pencil, put a horizontal line in the space provided (see sample question below).

7   There is **only one correct** answer to each question.

8   Any rough working should be done on the question paper or the rough working sheet, **not** on your answer sheet.

9   At the end of the exam, put the **answer sheet for Section A inside the front cover of this answer book**.

Sample Question

Plants compete mainly for

A   water, light and soil nutrients

B   water, food and soil nutrients

C   light, water and food

D   light, food and soil nutrients.

The correct answer is **A**—water, light and soil nutrients. The answer **A** has been clearly marked in **pencil** with a horizontal line (see below).

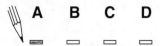

Changing an answer

If you decide to change your answer, carefully erase your first answer and using your pencil, fill in the answer you want. The answer below has been changed to **D**.

       A   **B**   **C**   **D**

SECTION A

All questions in this Section should be attempted.

1. The diagram below shows a cell.

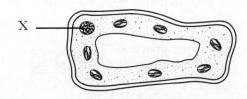

The function of structure X is to

A   control cell activities

B   keep the cell turgid

C   control entry and exit of material

D   release energy from glucose.

2. Fungi destroy bacteria by producing

A   antibiotics

B   alcohol

C   carbon dioxide

D   biogas.

3. The graph below shows the effect of temperature on the activity of the enzyme pepsin.

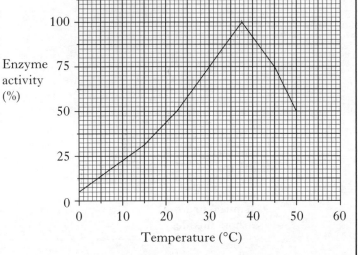

Between which two temperatures is there the greatest increase in enzyme activity?

A $0 – 10\,°C$

B $10 – 20\,°C$

C $20 – 30\,°C$

D $30 – 40\,°C$

4. In an investigation into the synthesis of starch from glucose-1-phosphate (G-1-P) by the enzyme phosphorylase, a tile was set up as shown below. Starch-free potato extract was used as the source of phosphorylase.

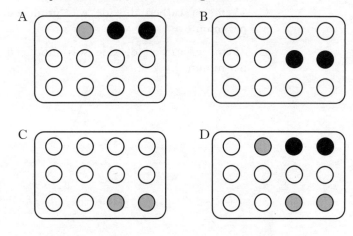

Iodine solution was added to the columns at the time intervals shown.

Which of the following tiles shows the expected result of this investigation?

[Turn over

5. An investigation was carried out to measure the rate of carbon dioxide production in bread dough.

    Carbon dioxide production was measured by recording the change in volume of a sample of bread dough over a 50 minute period.

    The results are shown in the table below.

Time (minutes)	0	10	20	30	40	50
Volume of dough (cm³)	10	14	18	21	23	25

    The conclusion for this investigation was

    A $0.3\,cm^3$ of carbon dioxide was produced per minute

    B $0.5\,cm^3$ of carbon dioxide was produced per minute

    C $15\,cm^3$ of carbon dioxide was produced per minute

    D $25\,cm^3$ of carbon dioxide was produced per minute.

6. The apparatus below was used to investigate respiration in germinating peas.

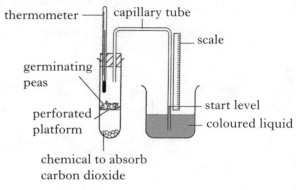

    A suitable control for this investigation would be

    A

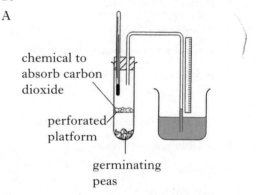

    B

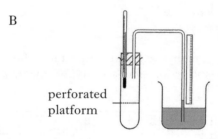

    C

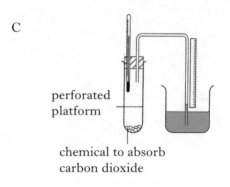

    D

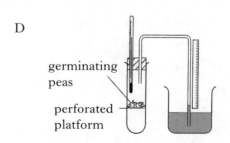

7. The graph shows the effect of varying the light intensity, temperature and carbon dioxide concentration on the rate of photosynthesis.

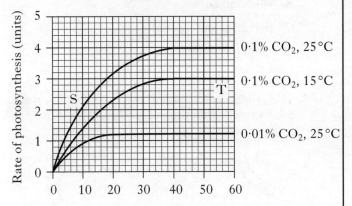

The rate of photosynthesis is being limited by

A   temperature at S and light intensity at T

B   light intensity at S and temperature at T

C   carbon dioxide at S and temperature at T

D   light intensity at S and carbon dioxide at T.

8. Which of the following conditions in a greenhouse would produce earlier crops?

A   Glass shading

B   Cool air conditioners

C   Additional oxygen

D   Additional carbon dioxide

9. The diagram below shows part of a food chain in the Arctic tundra.

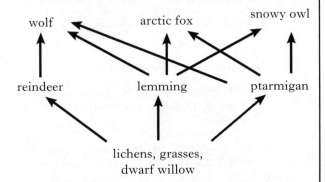

A population in this food web is all the

A   plants

B   reindeer

C   animals

D   living organisms.

10. The diagram below represents a field (Y) with an area (X) fenced off.

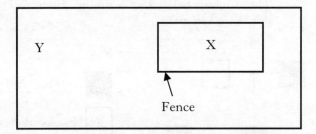

Sheep and rabbits provide very high intensity of grazing in area Y but cannot graze in fenced off area X.

Which line in the table below describes the diversity of plant species in areas X and Y after one year?

	Diversity of plant species	
	Area X	Area Y
A	higher	lower
B	lower	higher
C	higher	higher
D	lower	lower

11. The chromosome complement of a human individual who inherits an X-chromosome from their father is

A   44 including XX

B   44 including XY

C   46 including XX

D   46 including XY

[Turn over

12. In humans, the allele for free earlobes (E) is dominant to the allele for fixed earlobes (e).

The diagram below shows the inheritance of this characteristic.

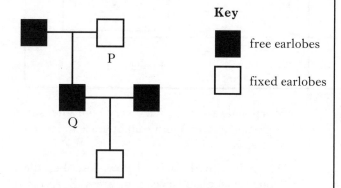

Key

☐ free earlobes (filled square)

☐ fixed earlobes (empty square)

Which line in the table identifies correctly the genotypes of persons P and Q?

	Genotype	
	P	Q
A	ee	EE
B	ee	Ee
C	EE	Ee
D	Ee	Ee

13. A hairy stemmed pea plant was crossed with a smooth stemmed pea plant and all of the F_1 had hairy stems.

The genotype of the hairy stemmed parent plant is

A heterozygous dominant

B heterozygous recessive

C homozygous recessive

D homozygous dominant.

14. In gerbils, agouti coat colour is dominant to white.

Some heterozygous gerbils were allowed to interbreed and 56 offspring were produced. What would be the expected number of agouti gerbils?

A 14

B 28

C 42

D 56

15. Skin colour in humans is an example of

A discontinuous variation

B co-dominance

C polygenic inheritance

D random assortment.

16. The diagram below shows stages in the production of a desired product by genetic engineering.

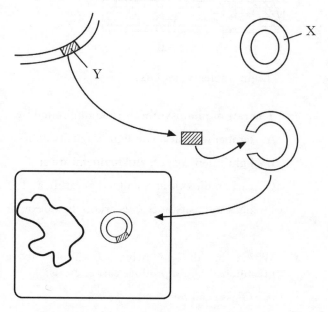

Which line in the table identifies correctly the structures labelled above?

	X	Y
A	bacterium	gene
B	plasmid	chromosome
C	bacterium	chromosome
D	plasmid	gene

17. Digestion takes place in animals

A and allows insoluble molecules to pass directly through the wall of the small intestine

B as enzymes cannot act on insoluble molecules

C and makes insoluble molecules into soluble molecules to allow absorption

D and allows food to be passed along the gut by peristalsis.

18. Salivary glands produce mucus to

A   lubricate the food in the stomach

B   lubricate the food to aid swallowing

C   protect the mouth from amylase

D   protect the oesophagus from amylase.

19. In the stomach, proteins are broken down into polypeptides.

The graph below shows the concentrations of protein and polypeptides in the stomach over 40 minutes.

●——————● Concentration of protein

✗------✗ Concentration of polypeptides

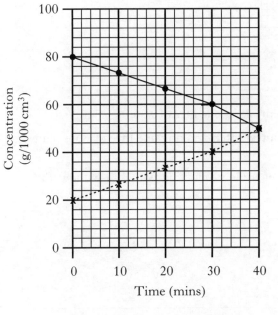

What was the ratio of protein concentration to polypeptide concentration after 30 minutes?

A   3 : 2

B   2 : 3

C   2 : 1

D   1 : 2

20. The diagram below shows some structures in a villus.

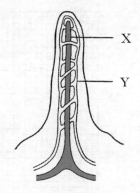

Which line in the table below correctly identifies the products of digestion which pass into structures X and Y?

	X	Y
A	glucose	amino acids
B	glycerol	fatty acids
C	amino acids	glycogen
D	fatty acids	glucose

21. Which line in the table identifies correctly the functions of the large intestine and the anus?

	Large intestine	*Anus*
A	digests food material	eliminates undigested material
B	stores undigested material	absorbs water from undigested material
C	absorbs water from undigested material	eliminates undigested material
D	absorbs digested food products	absorbs water from undigested material

22. The diagram below shows the human urinary system.

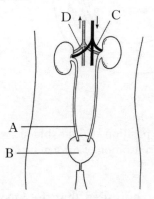

Which labelled part is the ureter?

23. The graph below shows the results of an investigation on the effect of ADH on urine production.

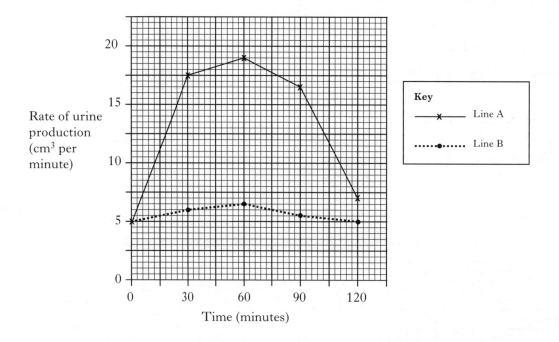

Line A shows the rate of urine production for a volunteer after drinking one litre of water.

Line B shows the rate of urine production from the same volunteer after drinking one litre of water and receiving an injection of ADH.

After 60 minutes, what was the difference between the rates of urine production with and without the ADH injection?

A   6·5 cm^3 per minute

B   12·5 cm^3 per minute

C   19·0 cm^3 per minute

D   25·5 cm^3 per minute

---

24. The diagram below shows an air sac with part of its capillary network.

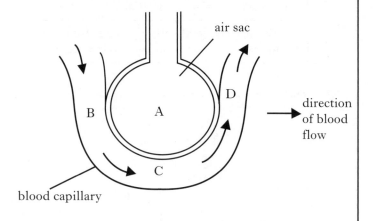

At which position would blood with the highest concentration of oxygen be found?

25. The diagram below shows a section through the human brain.

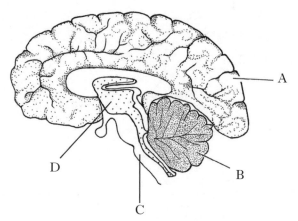

Which labelled part is the site of temperature regulation?

Candidates are reminded that the answer sheet for Section A MUST be placed INSIDE the front cover of this answer book.

DO NOT
WRITE IN
THIS
MARGIN

SECTION B

All questions in this section should be attempted.
All answers must be written clearly and legibly in ink.

Marks

1. (*a*) The diagram below shows three stages X, Y and Z that occur when an enzyme converts its substrate into a product.

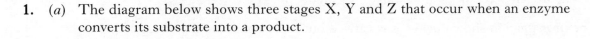

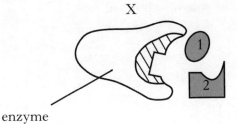 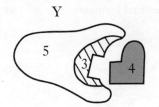 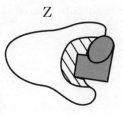

enzyme

(i) This enzyme promotes the breakdown of a complex molecule into simpler molecules.

Put the stages into the correct order to show this degradation reaction.

_____ ⟶ _____ ⟶ _____

1

(ii) Which number in the diagram shows the active site?

_____

1

(*b*) Complete the following sentence by underlining the correct word from the choice in brackets.

Enzymes are made of $\left\{ \begin{array}{l} \text{carbohydrate} \\ \text{fat} \\ \text{protein} \end{array} \right\}$.

1

(*c*) Describe what happens to an enzyme when it is denatured.

_____

_____

1

[Turn over

Marks

2. Liver contains the enzyme catalase which carries out the following reaction.

hydrogen peroxide ———▶ water + oxygen

The investigation shown below was carried out to demonstrate the effect of pH on catalase activity in liver.

Hydrogen peroxide of different pH values was added to 1 g of roughly chopped raw liver.

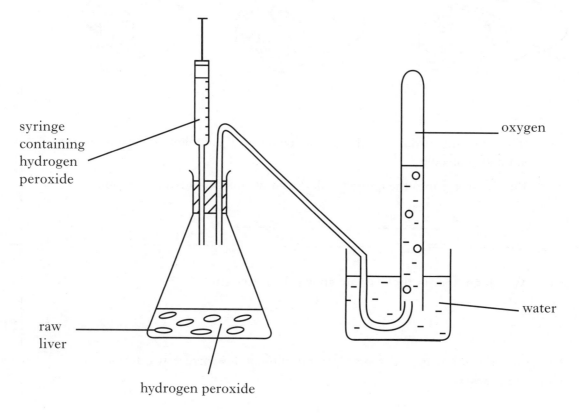

The time taken to collect 1cm³ of oxygen was recorded and the results are shown in the table below.

pH of hydrogen peroxide solution	Time to collect 1 cm³ of oxygen (seconds)			Average time to collect 1cm³ of oxygen (seconds)
	Trial 1	Trial 2	Trial 3	
7	76	77	81	78
8	56	58	57	57
9	50	45	40	45
10	53	50	53	52
11	59	69	70	66

(a) From the table, state the optimum pH for catalase in liver.

_____

1

Marks

2. **(continued)**

   (b) Name the variable altered in this investigation.

   _____   1

   (c) Explain why the experiment was repeated at each pH value and averages calculated.

   _____   1

   (d) Construct a line graph of the **average** time taken to collect 1 cm^3 of oxygen against pH of hydrogen peroxide solution.

   (Additional graph paper, if required, will be found on *Page thirty-two*)

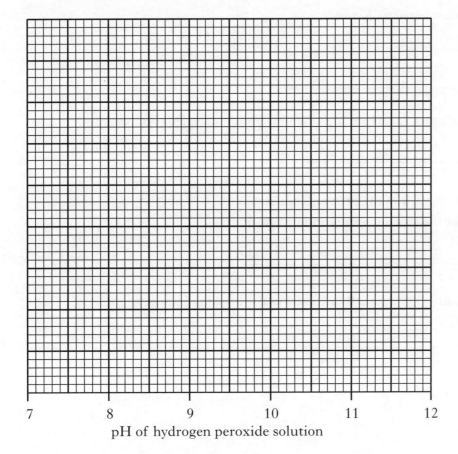

   pH of hydrogen peroxide solution

   2

   (e) Predict the average time to collect 1 cm^3 of oxygen at pH12.

   _____ seconds   1

   [Turn over

Marks

3. Yeast may carry out two different types of respiration.

   (*a*) Name the type of respiration in yeast which has the highest energy yield.

   _____   1

   (*b*) The diagram below shows one type of respiration in yeast cells.

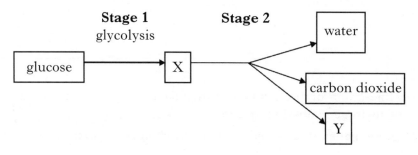

   (i) Name substances X and Y.

   X _____   1

   Y _____   1

   (ii) What other substance must be present for stage 2 to occur?

   _____   1

   (*c*) Yeast cells are used in the brewing industry.
   (i) Name the type of respiration involved.

   _____   1

   (ii) Explain why yeast cells are used in the brewing industry.

   _____   1

Marks

4. (*a*) The diagram below shows an investigation into the effect of adding three different solutions to three pieces of muscle tissue.

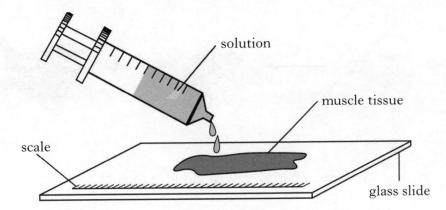

The results of the investigation are given in the table below.

Muscle tissue	Solution added	Length of muscle tissue			
		at start (mm)	after 5 minutes (mm)	difference in length (mm)	percentage difference (%)
1	1% glucose	50	50	0	0
2	1% ATP	45	41·5	4·5	10
3	0·5% ATP	48	45·6	2·4	

(i) Calculate the percentage difference in length for muscle tissue 3.

Space for calculation

_____% **1**

(ii) What conclusion can be drawn from the results?

_____

_____ **1**

(*b*) (i) What term is used to describe the effect of lactic acid build up in muscle tissue?

_____ **1**

(ii) How can lactic acid be removed from muscle tissue?

_____ **1**

Marks

5. (*a*)   The diagram below represents a food chain in a garden.

(*The organisms are not to scale.*)

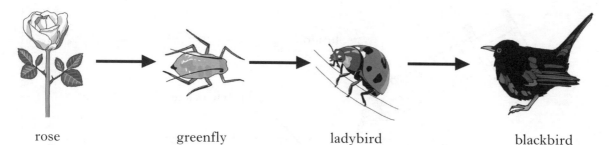

| rose bush | greenfly | ladybird | blackbird |

(i)   What term describes the greenfly in this food chain?

_____   1

(ii)   A rose bush contains $10\,000\,kJ/m^2/year$ of energy and only 10% of this energy is passed on at each stage of the food chain.

Use this information to complete the pyramid of energy below for this food chain.

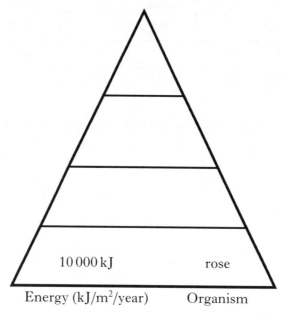

10 000 kJ   rose

Energy (kJ/m²/year)   Organism   2

(iii)   What happens to the energy that is **not** passed on at each stage of the food chain?

_____   1

(*b*)   Many ladybirds were seen over the summer in the garden.

They were able to interbreed and produce fertile offspring.

What can be concluded about the ladybirds, using all this information?

_____   1

Marks

6. The following table shows four blood groups and their frequency in a population.

Blood Group	Frequency in population (%)
O	44
A	42
B	10
AB	4

(a) Calculate the simplest whole number ratio of the frequency of blood groups O to AB.

Space for calculation

Blood group   _____ : _____
                    O   AB

1

(b) Name the type of variation shown by these blood groups.

_____

1

(c) Blood group is determined by three alleles A, B, O.

The table below shows the possible genotypes of each blood group.

Genotype	Blood group
OO	O
AO, AA	A
BO, BB	B
AB	AB

(i) Which of these alleles are co-dominant?

_____

1

(ii) Explain the meaning of co-dominant alleles.

_____

_____

1

Marks

7. (*a*) The diagram below shows a summary of events that occur during reproduction in a flowering plant.

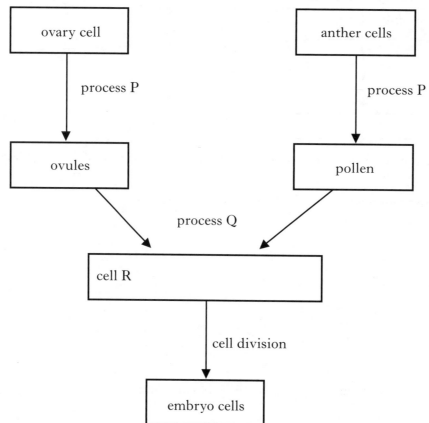

(i) **Complete the diagram** by entering the name of cell type R.   1

(ii) Which process in the diagram represents fertilisation?

_____   1

(iii) Complete the following table by inserting a tick (✔) in the correct boxes to show which of the cells in the diagram have a double or single set of chromosomes.

Cell	Double set of chromosomes	Single set of chromosomes
anther		
ovule		
R		
embryo		

2

Marks

7. (continued)

(*b*) Explain the need to produce cells with a single set of chromosomes in reproduction.

_____

_____   1

(*c*) <u>Underline</u> one option in each set of brackets to make the following sentence correct.

Random assortment of chromosomes occurs during $\left\{ \begin{array}{c} \text{meiosis} \\ \text{fertilisation} \end{array} \right\}$

which $\left\{ \begin{array}{c} \text{increases} \\ \text{decreases} \end{array} \right\}$ the $\left\{ \begin{array}{c} \text{biodiversity} \\ \text{variation} \end{array} \right\}$ of gametes.   2

[Turn over

Marks

8. An investigation to demonstrate the responses of woodlice to light was carried out in a choice chamber. Half of the choice chamber was covered in black paper and the other half left in light.

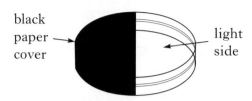

black paper cover

light side

Ten woodlice were introduced into the choice chamber. The number of woodlice in each side was counted every two minutes for ten minutes.

The graph shows the results of this investigation.

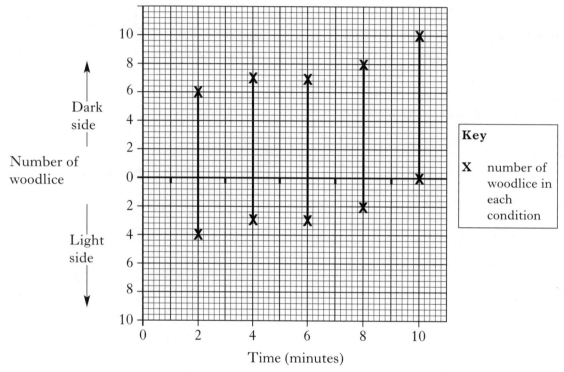

Key

X number of woodlice in each condition

Time (minutes)

(a) Name two environmental conditions that should be kept constant in this investigation.

1 _____

2 _____ **2**

(b) What conclusion can be made from the results of this investigation?

_____

_____ **1**

(c) Explain the advantage of this behaviour to the woodlice.

_____

_____ **1**

Marks

9. It is thought that Darwin's finches evolved from one type of ancestral finch.

The diagram below shows examples of different species of Darwin's finches.

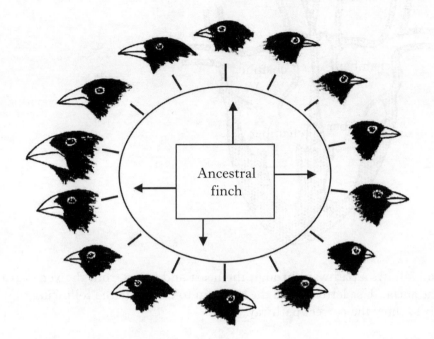

(a) (i) What **two** observations can be made from the diagram about the structure of the finches' beaks?

_____ 1

(ii) Name one environmental factor which has led to this variation.

_____ 1

(b) What term is used to describe the role that each finch plays within its community?

_____ 1

(c) The existence of some Darwin's finches is under threat in the Galapagos Islands due to human activity.

(i) Give an example of a human activity that could be affecting the finches.

_____ 1

(ii) What could be an effect of this human activity on finch biodiversity?

_____ 1

[Turn over

Marks

10. The diagram below shows a section through the heart.

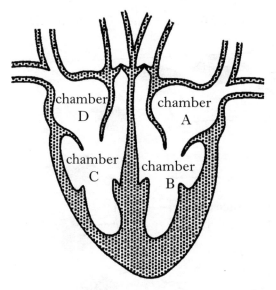

(*a*) (i) Blood follows a pathway through the heart and lungs from the vena cava to the aorta. Use letters from the diagram to complete the following flow chart to show the correct pathway.

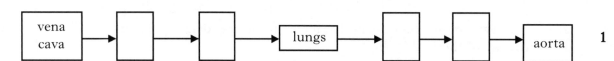

1

(ii) State the letter of a chamber of the heart which contains oxygenated blood.

Chamber _____

1

DO NOT WRITE IN THIS MARGIN

Marks

10. (continued)

(*b*) Decide if each of the following statements about the transport of gases by the bloodstream is **True** or **False**, and tick (✓) the appropriate box.

If the statement is **False** write the correct word in the **Correction box** to replace the word underlined in the statement.

Statement	*True*	*False*	*Correction*
Oxygen forms oxyhaemoglobin at low oxygen levels in the lungs.			
Carbon dioxide is transported in red blood cells.			
Carbon dioxide dissolved in the blood plasma decreases acidity.			

3

[Turn over

Marks

11. (*a*) An investigation was carried out to estimate the concentration of urea in two unknown urine samples. A tablet of the enzyme urease was added to a test tube containing the urine sample. When urease reacted with urea in the sample the gas produced turned moist litmus paper blue.

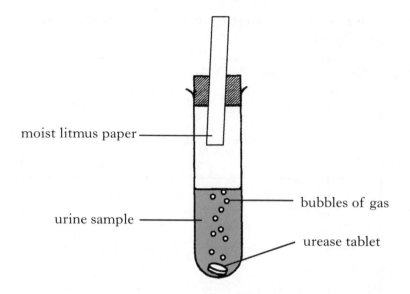

The time taken for the litmus paper to turn blue was recorded in each case.

The table below shows the results obtained when various urine samples of known and unknown urea concentration were tested.

Concentration of urea in urine sample (g/100 cm³)	Time taken for litmus paper to turn blue (seconds)
0·5	300
1·5	210
2·5	115
3·5	10
unknown A	75
unknown B	225

(i) Which unknown urine sample, A or B, has the lowest concentration of urea?

_____   **1**

(ii) Suggest a reason for a low concentration of urea in urine.

_____   **1**

Marks

11. **(*a*) (continued)**

(iii)   Predict the effect on the results if the temperature was increased from 20°C to 30°C in this investigation.

_____   1

(iv)   Describe a suitable control for this investigation.

_____   1

(*b*)   The diagram below shows the parts of a kidney nephron involved in filtration.

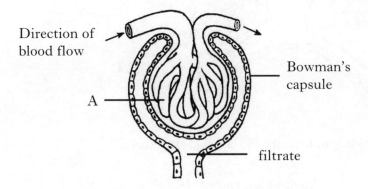

(i)   Name part A which consists of a bundle of blood capillaries.

_____   1

(ii)   Describe the process which forms urine from the filtrate.

_____

_____   1

[Turn over

Marks

12. (*a*) The diagram below shows the human breathing system.

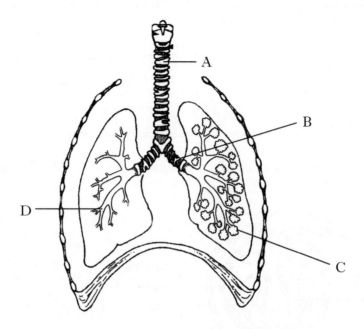

Complete the table below to identify the labelled structures.

Letter	Name of structure
	bronchiole
B	
	trachea
C	

2

Marks

12. (continued)

(b) A person breathed normally, took deep breaths, then returned to normal breathing.

The volume of air in the lungs was measured and the results are shown in the graph below.

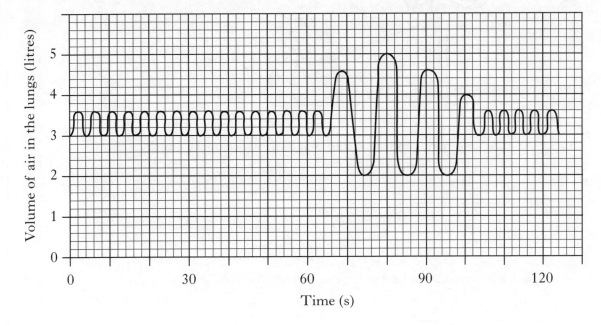

(i) What was the normal breathing rate for this person?

_____ breaths per minute   1

(ii) What was the highest volume of air inhaled in a single breath?

_____ litres   1

[Turn over

Marks

13. (a) The diagram below shows parts of the central nervous system (CNS) and a nerve to the heart.

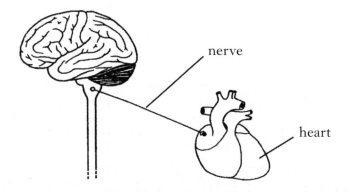

(i) Name the two parts, shown in the diagram, which make up the central nervous system (CNS).

1 _____

2 _____   **1**

(ii) Name the area, shown in the diagram, which controls heart rate.

_____   **1**

(b) Reflex arcs contain relay fibres.

(i) Which structure sends impulses to the relay fibre?

_____   **1**

(ii) What is the function of relay fibres in a reflex arc?

_____   **1**

(c) Explain the function of a reflex response.

_____

_____   **1**

[Turn over for Section C on *page twenty-eight*

SECTION C

Marks

Both questions in this section should be attempted.

Note that each question contains a choice.

**Questions 1 and 2 should be attempted on the blank pages which follow.
All answers must be written clearly and legibly in ink.**

Supplementary sheets, if required, may be obtained from the invigilator.

1. Answer **either** A **or** B.

    A. The diagrams below show the two stages of photosynthesis.

    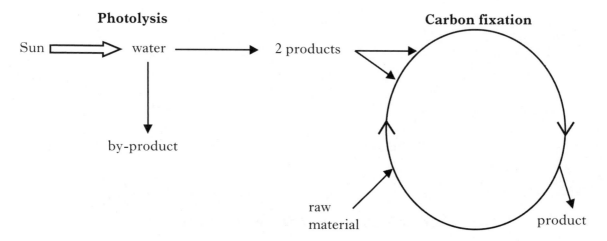

    Describe what happens during the two stages

    (a) photolysis

    and

    (b) carbon fixation.

    5

OR

    B. The diagrams below show animal and plant cells in isotonic solutions.
    These diagrams are not to scale.

    Animal cells Plant cells

    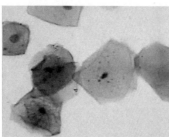 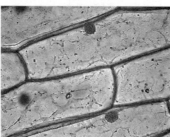

    Describe the osmotic effect of transferring

    (a) the animal cells into a hypotonic solution (water)

    (b) the plant cells into a hypertonic solution (strong salt).

    5

    Question 2 is on *Page thirty*

SPACE FOR ANSWER TO QUESTION 1

[Turn over for Question 2 on *Page thirty*

DO NOT WRITE IN THIS MARGIN

Marks

2. Answer **either** A **or** B.

Labelled diagrams may be included where appropriate.

A. Describe the role of the liver and pancreas in digestion. Include in your answer the processing of absorbed materials such as glucose and amino acids. **5**

OR

B. Describe the role of antibodies and phagocytosis in defence. Name the cells involved in each of these defence mechanisms. **5**

[*END OF QUESTION PAPER*]

SPACE FOR ANSWER TO QUESTION 2

ADDITIONAL SPACE FOR ANSWERS

ADDITIONAL GRAPH PAPER FOR QUESTION 2(*d*)

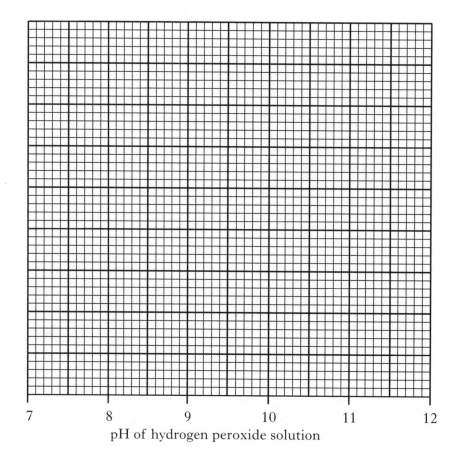

pH of hydrogen peroxide solution

ADDITIONAL SPACE FOR ANSWERS

ADDITIONAL SPACE FOR ANSWERS

[BLANK PAGE]

FOR OFFICIAL USE

Total for
Sections B and C

X007/201

NATIONAL
QUALIFICATIONS
2010

THURSDAY, 27 MAY
9.00 AM – 11.00 AM

BIOLOGY
INTERMEDIATE 2

Fill in these boxes and read what is printed below.

Full name of centre

Town

Forename(s)

Surname

Date of birth

Day   Month   Year   Scottish candidate number   Number of seat

SECTION A (25 marks)

Instructions for completion of Section A are given on page two.

For this section of the examination you must use an HB pencil.

SECTIONS B AND C (75 marks)

1   (a) All questions should be attempted.

    (b) It should be noted that in **Section C** questions 1 and 2 each contain a choice.

2   The questions may be answered in any order but all answers are to be written in the spaces provided in this answer book, **and must be written clearly and legibly in ink**.

3   Additional space for answers will be found at the end of the book. If further space is required, supplementary sheets may be obtained from the Invigilator and should be inserted inside the **front** cover of this book.

4   The numbers of questions must be clearly inserted with any answers written in the additional space.

5   Rough work, if any should be necessary, should be written in this book and then scored through when the fair copy has been written. If further space is required, a supplementary sheet for rough work may be obtained from the Invigilator.

6   Before leaving the examination room you must give this book to the Invigilator. If you do not, you may lose all the marks for this paper.

Read carefully

1 Check that the answer sheet provided is for **Biology Intermediate 2 (Section A)**.

2 For this section of the examination you must use an **HB pencil** and, where necessary, an eraser.

3 Check that the answer sheet you have been given has **your name**, **date of birth**, **SCN** (Scottish Candidate Number) and **Centre Name** printed on it.

Do not change any of these details.

4 If any of this information is wrong, tell the Invigilator immediately.

5 If this information is correct, **print** your name and seat number in the boxes provided.

6 The answer to each question is **either** A, B, C or D. Decide what your answer is, then, using your pencil, put a horizontal line in the space provided (see sample question below).

7 There is **only one correct** answer to each question.

8 Any rough working should be done on the question paper or the rough working sheet, **not** on your answer sheet.

9 At the end of the exam, put the **answer sheet for Section A inside the front cover of this answer book**.

Sample Question

Plants compete mainly for

A water, light and soil nutrients

B water, food and soil nutrients

C light, water and food

D light, food and soil nutrients.

The correct answer is **A**—water, light and soil nutrients. The answer **A** has been clearly marked in **pencil** with a horizontal line (see below).

Changing an answer

If you decide to change your answer, carefully erase your first answer and using your pencil, fill in the answer you want. The answer below has been changed to **D**.

A B C D

SECTION A

All questions in this Section should be attempted.

1. Four thin sections of onion tissue were immersed in 5% sugar solution.

   The sections were left for 15 minutes then viewed under a microscope.

   The table below shows the percentage of cells plasmolysed in each section.

Section	Cells plasmolysed (%)
1	44
2	44
3	54
4	58

   The average percentage of cells plasmolysed is

   A   44

   B   50

   C   54

   D   200.

2. The diagram below shows the initial diameter of a potato disc.

   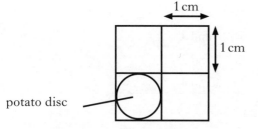

   potato disc

   The potato disc was placed in a hypotonic solution for one hour.

   Which of the following diagrams shows correctly the change in the diameter of the potato disc?

   A 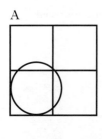   B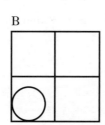

   C 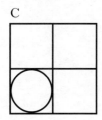   D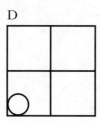

3. One of the properties of enzymes in the initiation of chemical reactions is that an enzyme

   A   does not alter the energy input required

   B   raises the energy input required

   C   lowers the energy input required

   D   raises then lowers the energy input required.

4. Which term refers to the process by which complex molecules are formed from simple molecules?

   A   Digestion

   B   Synthesis

   C   Degradation

   D   Respiration

5. Which of the following correctly describes amylase?

   A   It breaks down starch into amino acids.

   B   It builds up glucose-1-phosphate into starch.

   C   It breaks down proteins into peptides.

   D   It breaks down starch into maltose.

6. A plant cell, which was placed in a liquid, gained water by osmosis.

   When compared to the liquid, the cell contents are described as being

   A   plasmolysed

   B   hypertonic

   C   hypotonic

   D   flaccid.

7. Which of the following increases in the muscles of an athlete and causes muscle fatigue during a race?

   A   Lactic acid

   B   Glucose

   C   Oxygen

   D   ATP

8. The following experiment was set up.

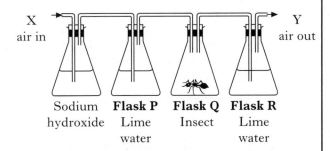

X
air in

Y
air out

Sodium
hydroxide

Flask P
Lime
water

Flask Q
Insect

Flask R
Lime
water

Sodium hydroxide solution absorbs carbon dioxide from air.

Lime water turns from clear to cloudy in the presence of carbon dioxide.

Air is drawn through the apparatus from X to Y, passing through each flask in turn.

Predict what would happen to the results if two insects were used in flask Q. The lime water in

A Flask P turns cloudy more slowly

B Flask P turns cloudy more quickly

C Flask R turns cloudy more slowly

D Flask R turns cloudy more quickly.

9. The diagrams below show four experiments used to investigate the conditions needed for photosynthesis.

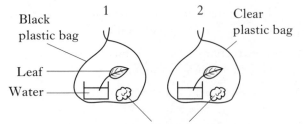

Black
plastic bag

1

2

Clear
plastic bag

Leaf

Water

Cotton wool soaked in a chemical
that produces carbon dioxide

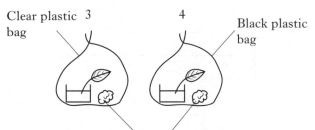

Clear plastic
bag

3

4

Black plastic
bag

Cotton wool soaked in a chemical
that absorbs carbon dioxide

After two days, the four leaves were tested for the presence of starch.

The results from which two experiments should be compared to show that carbon dioxide is needed for photosynthesis?

A 1 and 2

B 2 and 4

C 2 and 3

D 3 and 4

10. A species can be defined as a group of organisms which

A breed together to produce fertile offspring

B have the same phenotypes

C contain the same number of chromosomes

D contain identical genetic material.

11. The graph below shows the average number of peppered moths, in a woodland, in June of each year over a 10 year period.

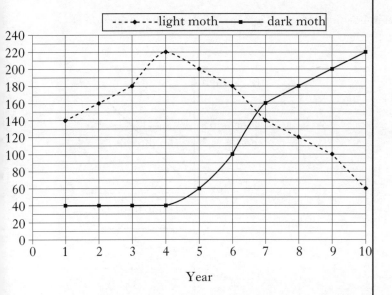

Year

Studies have shown that an increase in the number of dark moths is related to an increase in the level of pollution in the atmosphere.

Which of the following best describes what would happen to the number of moths if measures were introduced to reduce air pollution in year 10?

	Light moth	Dark moth
A	decrease	increase
B	increase	decrease
C	increase	increase
D	decrease	decrease

12. The diagram below shows the main parts of a flower.

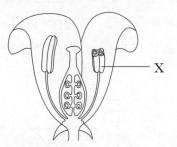

Which line in the table identifies X and the type of gamete it produces?

	Name of X	Type of gamete produced
A	ovary	male
B	ovary	female
C	anther	female
D	anther	male

13. The diagram below shows a stage in the process of reproduction.

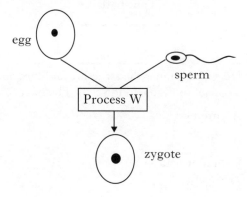

Process W is

A meiosis

B fertilisation

C gamete production

D random assortment.

[Turn over

14. Sperm production in humans is controlled by two hormones, P and Q.

As levels of P rise, sperm production increases.

As levels of Q rise, sperm production decreases.

Which of the graphs below shows the changes in hormone levels of a man whose sperm production is decreasing?

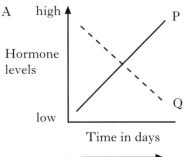

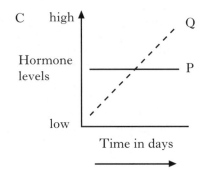

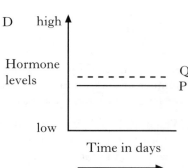

15. DNA determines the structure and function of a type of molecule in the cell. The molecule is

A   protein

B   fat

C   amino acid

D   carbohydrate.

16. In humans, the allele for blood group A is dominant to the allele for blood group O.

Two parents both have blood group A. Their child has blood group O.

What is the best explanation for this pattern of inheritance?

A   The child has inherited the blood group directly from a grandparent.

B   The parents are homozygous for the blood group alleles.

C   The parents are heterozygous for the blood group alleles.

D   There has been a mutation in the blood group alleles.

17. Which line in the table below identifies correctly one advantage and one disadvantage of genetic engineering to make desired products?

	Advantage	*Disadvantage*
A	increased rate of production	cost of development
B	cost of development	possible release of genetically engineered bacteria into the environment
C	increased range of products	increased rate of production
D	increased rate of production	increased range of products

18. The table below shows the composition of a $200\,cm^3$ serving of low fat milk.

Composition	$200\,cm^3$ low fat milk provides
protein	6·0 g
carbohydrate	10·0 g
fat	0·2 g

What is the simplest whole number ratio of the mass of protein to carbohydrate to fat?

A   3 :   5 : 0·1

B   6 : 10 : 0·2

C   30 : 50 : 1

D   60 : 100 : 2

19. The table below shows the composition of inhaled air and exhaled air.

	Inhaled air (%)	Exhaled air (%)
Oxygen	20	16
Carbon dioxide	0·04	4

How many times greater is the oxygen concentration in inhaled air than in exhaled air?

A   0·08

B   1·25

C   4

D   320

20. The list below refers to features of a capillary network.

1   It has a large surface area.

2   It is in close contact with tissue cells.

3   Capillaries are thin walled.

Which statements refer to features that allow efficient gas exchange?

A   1 and 2 only

B   1 and 3 only

C   2 and 3 only

D   1, 2 and 3

21. The graph below shows the relationship between oxygen concentration and the concentration of oxyhaemoglobin.

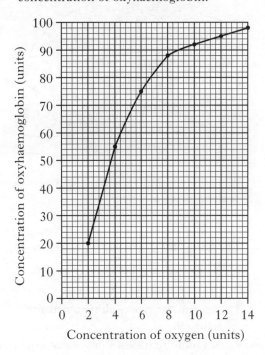

What is the percentage increase in the concentration of oxyhaemoglobin when the concentration of oxygen increases from 2 units to 4 units?

A   2

B   35

C   55

D   175

22. Which of the following produce antibodies?

A   Blood plasma

B   Lymphocytes

C   Macrophages

D   Red blood cells

[Turn over

23. The diagram below shows a human brain.

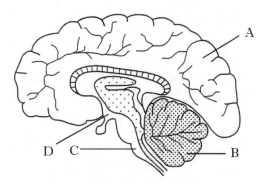

Which letter shows the site that controls heart rate and breathing rate?

24. The following stages occur in a reflex action.

1   The effector produces a response.

2   A sense organ is stimulated.

3   An impulse passes along a sensory neurone.

4   An impulse passes along a motor neurone.

The correct order of the stages is

A   2, 3, 4, 1

B   2, 1, 4, 3

C   1, 2, 3, 4

D   3, 4, 1, 2.

25. Which of the following pathways shows the correct response by blood vessels in the skin to a decrease in body temperature?

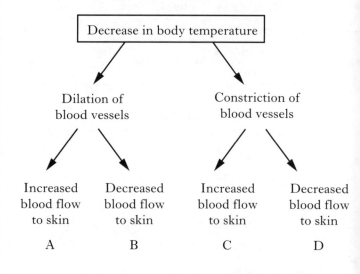

Candidates are reminded that the answer sheet for Section A MUST be placed INSIDE the front cover of this answer book.

[Turn over for Section B on *Page ten*

Marks

SECTION B

All questions in this section should be attempted.
All answers must be written clearly and legibly in ink.

1. (*a*) The diagram below shows two cells P and Q.

Cell P Cell Q

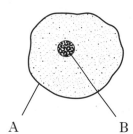 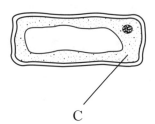

A   B   C

(i) Complete the table below to give the name and function of the parts labelled A, B and C.

Letter	Part	Function
A	cell membrane	
B	nucleus	
C		site of cell activities

2

(ii) Which cell is a plant cell? Give a reason for your choice.

Cell _____

Reason _____

1

(*b*) Cells have commercial and industrial uses.

(i) One type of cell is used in the production of yoghurt.

(A) Name the type of cell used in the production of yoghurt.

_____

1

(B) Name the milk sugar used by these cells.

_____

1

DO NOT WRITE IN THIS MARGIN

Marks

1. **(b)** **(continued)**

(ii) <u>Underline</u> **one** option in each set of brackets to make the following sentence correct.

Gasohol is produced when cells act on sugar to produce $\left\{ \begin{array}{c} \text{alcohol} \\ \text{methane} \end{array} \right\}$

which is then mixed with $\left\{ \begin{array}{c} \text{ethanol} \\ \text{petrol} \end{array} \right\}$.

1

(iii) Fungal cells are used to produce antibiotics. What is the function of antibiotics in the treatment of disease?

_____

1

[Turn over

Marks

2. (*a*) Liver contains the enzyme catalase. A piece of liver was added to hydrogen peroxide and foam was produced as shown below.

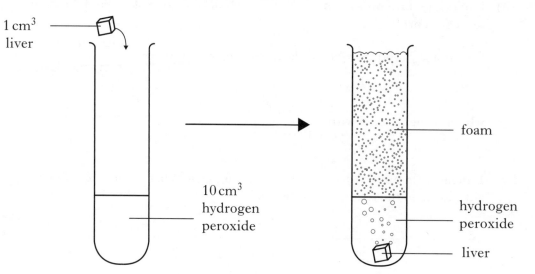

1 cm³
liver

10 cm³
hydrogen
peroxide

foam

hydrogen
peroxide

liver

(i) Name the gas in the foam.

_____   **1**

(ii) Which other product was formed during this reaction?

_____   **1**

(iii) Describe a control which would be used to show that active catalase is needed for this experiment.

_____

_____   **1**

(iv) How could the activity of catalase be measured in this experiment?

_____

_____   **1**

Marks

2. **(continued)**

   (b) The diagram below shows an investigation to compare the activity of catalase in apple and liver.

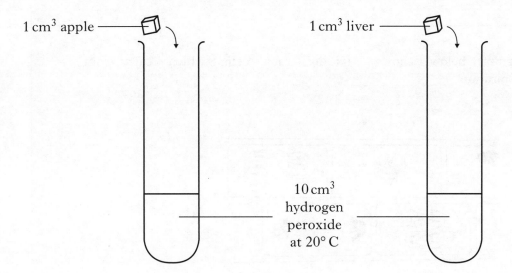

1 cm³ apple   1 cm³ liver

10 cm³
hydrogen
peroxide
at 20° C

   State **two** variables, not shown in the diagram, that must be kept constant for a valid comparison.

   1 _____

   2 _____   2

   (c) Explain why enzyme activity decreases at temperatures above the optimum.

   _____

   _____   1

[Turn over

Marks

3. (*a*) Cells need ATP for cell division. ATP is produced during the aerobic respiration of glucose.

How many ATP molecules are produced per glucose molecule in this process?

_____

1

(*b*) The diagram below shows dividing root cells which carry out aerobic respiration.

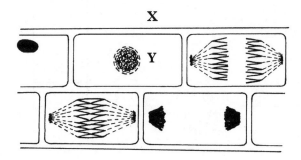

Carbon dioxide is one waste product of aerobic respiration.

Tick (✓) the appropriate box below to show the direction of diffusion of carbon dioxide.

X ⟶ Y ☐

Y ⟶ X ☐

1

(*c*) Aerobic respiration occurs in two stages. Name the first stage of aerobic respiration and a product, other than ATP.

Name _____

1

Product _____

1

Marks

4. The graph below shows the effects of two different environmental factors on the rate of photosynthesis.

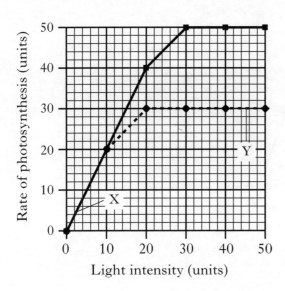

High concentration of carbon dioxide

Low concentration of carbon dioxide

(*a*) What are the limiting factors at points X and Y?

X _____   1

Y _____   1

(*b*) Suggest **one** way that the rate of photosynthesis can be measured.

_____

_____   1

(*c*) During the first stage of photosynthesis, light energy is used.

(i) Where is light energy trapped in the cell?

_____   1

(ii) State **one** use of this light energy.

_____   1

(*d*) (i) Name the second stage of photosynthesis.

_____   1

(ii) Name the carbohydrate produced during the second stage of photosynthesis.

_____   1

Marks

5. The diagram below shows part of an Antarctic food web.

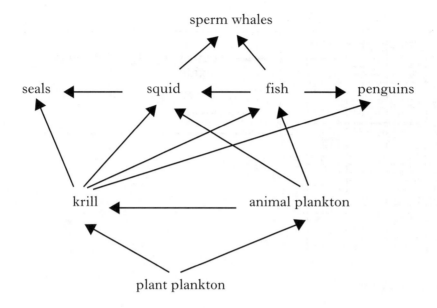

(*a*) Explain why a decrease in sperm whale numbers may lead to an increase in seal numbers.

_____

_____   1

(*b*) Decide if each of the following statements is **True** or **False**, and tick (✓) the appropriate box.

If the statement is **False**, write the correct word in the **Correction box** to replace the word(s) underlined in the statement.

Statement	True	False	Correction
In this food web, krill are herbivores.			
The population of sperm whales has the highest biomass.			
The range of species in a population is called biodiversity.			

3

Marks

6. (*a*) In shorthorn cattle, the allele for red coat colour (R) is co-dominant with the allele for white coat colour (W). Heterozygous shorthorn cattle have a mixture of red and white hairs and are described as "roan".

   (i) State the genotype of white cattle.

   _____   1

   (ii) A red female and roan male were crossed. Complete the Punnett square below to show the expected results of this cross.

	Genotype of gametes of roan male	
Genotype of gametes of red female R		
R		

2

(*b*) Seed mass in plants is controlled by several genes. Name this type of inheritance.

_____   1

(*c*) Decide if each of the following human characteristics shows **continuous** or **discontinuous** variation. Tick (✓) the appropriate boxes.

Human characteristic	*Type of variation*	
	continuous	*discontinuous*
Blood group		
Height		

1

(*d*) As an organism grows and develops, it is affected by environmental impact. What is the meaning of the term environmental impact?

_____

_____   1

Marks

7. Four groups of students investigated the effect of light intensity on the time taken for larvae to travel 10 cm. The light intensity was varied by moving the light source. The diagram below shows the apparatus.

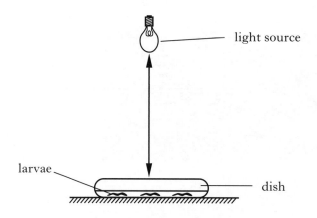

The table below shows the results of this investigation.

Light intensity	Time taken for larvae to travel 10 cm (s)				
	Group 1	*Group 2*	*Group 3*	*Group 4*	*Average*
High	20	22	24	22	22
Medium	39	42	47	44	43
Low	48	50	50	52	50
Very low	66	70	64	76	

(a) Complete the table to show the average time taken to travel 10 cm in very low light intensity.

Space for calculation

1

(b) Which light intensity showed the greatest **range** of results?

_____

1

7. (continued)

(*c*) On the grid below, plot a **bar graph** to show the **average** time taken for larvae to travel 10 cm in high, medium and low light intensity levels **only**.

(Additional graph paper, if required, will be found on *Page thirty*.)

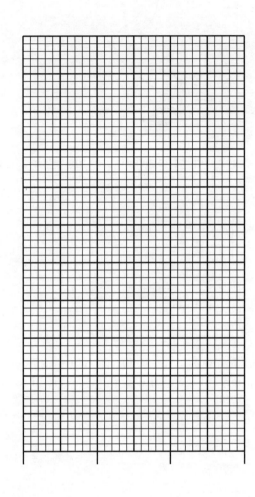

Average time taken for larvae to travel 10 cm (s)

3

(*d*) Describe the relationship between light intensity and time taken for larvae to travel 10 cm.

_____

_____ 1

[Turn over

Marks

8. Swans and cygnets (young swans) live on the River Ayr. Foxes in the area kill and eat cygnets.

(a) (i) <u>Underline</u> **one** option in each set of brackets to make the following sentences correct.

Cygnets are the $\begin{Bmatrix} \text{predators} \\ \text{prey} \end{Bmatrix}$ of foxes.

The foxes are $\begin{Bmatrix} \text{primary} \\ \text{secondary} \end{Bmatrix}$ consumers.

1

(ii) Fifty cygnets were counted in 2008. By 2009, 18 of these cygnets had been killed by foxes. What percentage of the cygnets survived to 2009?

Space for calculation

_____ %   1

(b) Dead adult swans were found throughout the year. It was discovered that the use of lead weights by anglers was poisoning the swans. Other animals in the river were also affected by the lead.

Suggest the effect of the lead on the biodiversity of a river ecosystem.

Explain your answer.

Effect _____

Explanation _____

_____   1

(c) State another type of pollution which may affect biodiversity in the river.

_____   1

Marks

9. The diagram below shows the human digestive system.

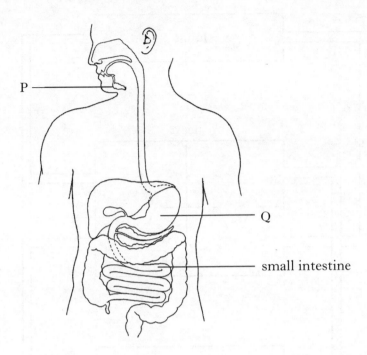

P

Q

small intestine

(*a*) Name the digestive enzymes produced by P and Q.

P _____   1

Q _____   1

(*b*) Describe how the action of peristalsis moves food through the small intestine.

_____

_____

_____   2

(*c*) Give **two** features of the small intestine which increases the rate of absorption.

1 _____   1

2 _____   1

[Turn over

Marks

10. The diagram below represents the human circulatory system.

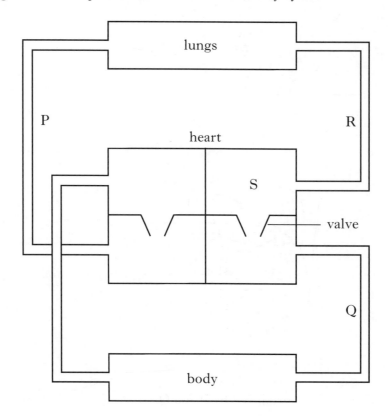

(a) (i) Draw arrows at P and Q to show the direction of blood flow in these vessels.

1

(ii) State whether the blood is oxygenated or deoxygenated in vessels P and Q.

P _____

Q _____

1

(b) Name heart chamber S and blood vessel R.

Heart chamber S _____

1

Blood vessel R _____

1

(c) What is the function of the heart valves?

_____

1

(d) Explain why a blocked coronary artery damages heart muscle.

_____

_____

1

Marks

11. The following diagram represents a kidney nephron.

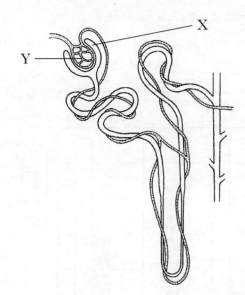

(a) The following sentences describe some processes that occur in the nephron.

Underline **one** option in each set of brackets to make the sentences correct.

The glomerulus is shown by letter $\left\{ \begin{array}{c} \text{X} \\ \text{Y} \end{array} \right\}$ and the process carried out in this

structure is $\left\{ \begin{array}{c} \text{absorption} \\ \text{filtration} \end{array} \right\}$.

An increase in the hormone ADH causes $\left\{ \begin{array}{c} \text{less} \\ \text{more} \end{array} \right\}$ water to be taken back into

the blood.   2

(b) Urea is the nitrogenous waste product removed in the urine.

Where is urea produced?

_____   1

(c) What term is used for the control of water content in organisms?

_____   1

[Turn over

Marks

12. A scientist measured the reaction times of five students before and after drinking alcohol.

Average reaction times were calculated for each student.

The graph below shows their average reaction times before and after drinking alcohol.

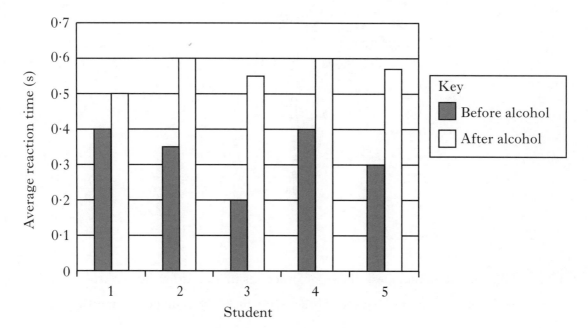

(*a*) What conclusion can be drawn from the results?

_____

_____ **1**

(*b*) Why did the scientist calculate the **average** reaction times?

_____

_____ **1**

(*c*) What is the percentage increase in the average reaction time for student 4 after drinking alcohol?

Space for calculation

_____ % **1**

(*d*) In this investigation, the students had to press a switch when a light flashed.

Which part of the brain coordinates this movement?

_____ **1**

[Turn over for Section C on *Page twenty-six*

Marks

SECTION C

Both questions in this section should be attempted.

Note that each question contains a choice.

**Questions 1 and 2 should be attempted on the blank pages which follow.
All answers must be written clearly and legibly in ink.**

Supplementary sheets, if required, may be obtained from the Invigilator.

1. Answer **either** A **or** B.

    A. The diagrams below show structures which are involved in the transport of oxygen.

    Lungs   Air sac   Capillary bed in the skin

    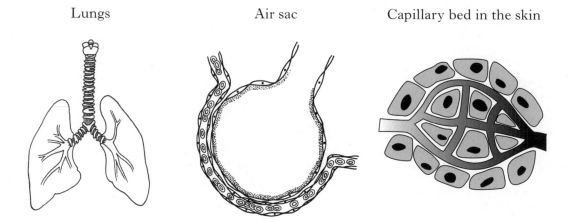

    Describe the path taken by oxygen through these structures from the air to a skin cell.   5

    OR

    B. The diagrams below represent the complex molecules of the three main food groups.

    Carbohydrate   Fat   Protein

    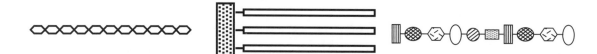

    Give a role of each food group and describe these three molecules in terms of their chemical elements and simple structures.   5

    Question 2 is on *Page twenty-eight*.

SPACE FOR ANSWER TO QUESTION 1

[Turn over for Question 2 on *Page twenty-eight*

DO NOT
WRITE IN
THIS
MARGIN

Marks

2. Answer **either** A **or** B.

    Labelled diagrams may be included where appropriate.

    A. Describe **three** structural adaptations of desert plants and explain how these adaptations increase their chances of survival.   **5**

    OR

    B. Describe the differences between the chromosomes in human body cells and human gametes.   Explain how these chromosomes are involved in sex determination.   **5**

[END OF QUESTION PAPER]

2. Answer **either** A **or** B.

SPACE FOR ANSWER TO QUESTION 2

ADDITIONAL SPACE FOR ANSWERS

ADDITIONAL GRAPH PAPER FOR QUESTION 7(c)

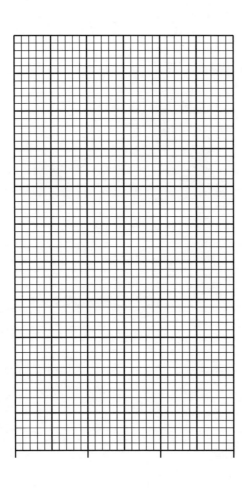

Average time taken for larvae to travel 10 cm (s)

[BLANK PAGE]

FOR OFFICIAL USE

Total for
Sections B and C

X007/201

NATIONAL
QUALIFICATIONS
2011

WEDNESDAY, 1 JUNE
9.00 AM – 11.00 AM

BIOLOGY
INTERMEDIATE 2

Fill in these boxes and read what is printed below.

Full name of centre

Town

Forename(s)

Surname

Date of birth

Day   Month   Year   Scottish candidate number   Number of seat

SECTION A (25 marks)

Instructions for completion of Section A are given on page two.

For this section of the examination you must use an HB pencil.

SECTIONS B AND C (75 marks)

1   (a)   All questions should be attempted.

   (b)   It should be noted that in **Section C** questions 1 and 2 each contain a choice.

2   The questions may be answered in any order but all answers are to be written in the spaces provided in this answer book, **and must be written clearly and legibly in ink**.

3   Additional space for answers will be found at the end of the book. If further space is required, supplementary sheets may be obtained from the Invigilator and should be inserted inside the **front** cover of this book.

4   The numbers of questions must be clearly inserted with any answers written in the additional space.

5   Rough work, if any should be necessary, should be written in this book and then scored through when the fair copy has been written. If further space is required, a supplementary sheet for rough work may be obtained from the Invigilator.

6   Before leaving the examination room you must give this book to the Invigilator. If you do not, you may lose all the marks for this paper.

Read carefully

1   Check that the answer sheet provided is for **Biology Intermediate 2 (Section A)**.

2   For this section of the examination you must use an **HB pencil** and, where necessary, an eraser.

3   Check that the answer sheet you have been given has **your name**, **date of birth**, **SCN** (Scottish Candidate Number) and **Centre Name** printed on it.

    Do not change any of these details.

4   If any of this information is wrong, tell the Invigilator immediately.

5   If this information is correct, **print** your name and seat number in the boxes provided.

6   The answer to each question is **either** A, B, C or D. Decide what your answer is, then, using your pencil, put a horizontal line in the space provided (see sample question below).

7   There is **only one correct** answer to each question.

8   Any rough working should be done on the question paper or the rough working sheet, **not** on your answer sheet.

9   At the end of the exam, put the **answer sheet for Section A inside the front cover of this answer book**.

Sample Question

Plants compete mainly for

A   water, light and soil nutrients

B   water, food and soil nutrients

C   light, water and food

D   light, food and soil nutrients.

The correct answer is **A**—water, light and soil nutrients. The answer **A** has been clearly marked in **pencil** with a horizontal line (see below).

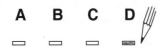

Changing an answer

If you decide to change your answer, carefully erase your first answer and using your pencil, fill in the answer you want. The answer below has been changed to **D**.

SECTION A

All questions in this Section should be attempted.

1. Which substance enters animal cells by diffusion and is used to produce ATP?

   A   Carbon dioxide

   B   Starch

   C   Water

   D   Glucose

2. The diagram below shows a model cell that was set up to investigate diffusion through a selectively permeable membrane.

   Iodine is a small, soluble molecule.

   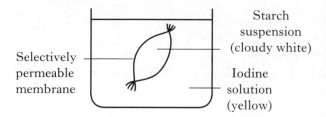

   Predict the colour changes which would be observed after one hour.

	Colour change after one hour	
	Starch suspension	Iodine solution
A	remained cloudy white	yellow to blue/black
B	cloudy white to blue/black	remained yellow
C	remained cloudy white	remained yellow
D	cloudy white to blue/black	yellow to blue/black

3. The diagram below shows energy transfer within a cell.

   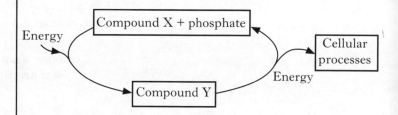

   Which line in the table identifies correctly compounds X and Y?

	X	Y
A	glucose	CO_2
B	CO_2	ADP
C	ADP	ATP
D	ATP	glucose

4. Which of the following stages in respiration would result in the production of 38 molecules of ATP?

   A   Glucose to pyruvic acid

   B   Pyruvic acid to lactic acid

   C   Pyruvic acid to carbon dioxide and water

   D   Glucose to carbon dioxide and water

[Turn over

5. The diagrams below show four experiments used in an investigation into the conditions needed for photosynthesis.

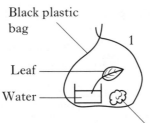

Black plastic bag

Leaf

Water

1

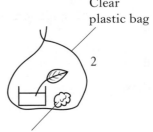

Clear plastic bag

2

Cotton wool soaked in a chemical that **produces** carbon dioxide

Clear plastic bag

3

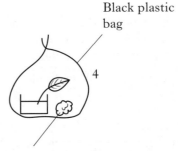

Black plastic bag

4

Cotton wool soaked in a chemical that **absorbs** carbon dioxide

The results from which two experiments should be compared to show that light is needed for photosynthesis?

A 1 and 2

B 1 and 4

C 2 and 3

D 3 and 4

6. The graph below shows the rate of photosynthesis, as light intensity increases, at two different temperatures.

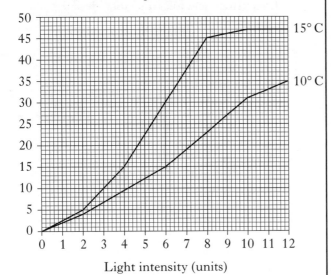

Rate of photosynthesis (Bubbles per minute)

Light intensity (units)

At a light intensity of 6 units, what is the simplest whole number ratio of the rate of photosynthesis at 10°C compared to 15°C?

A 15 : 30

B 10 : 15

C 3 : 6

D 1 : 2

7. A crop of tomatoes was grown in a polytunnel.

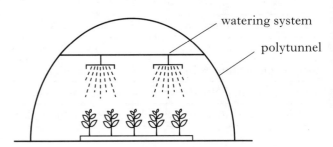

watering system

polytunnel

Which of the following changes would **not** produce an earlier crop of tomatoes?

A Increasing the heating during the day.

B Increasing the CO_2 concentration at night.

C Increasing the light intensity at night.

D Increasing the CO_2 concentration during the day.

8. An experiment was carried out to investigate the growth of plants for 40 days after germination.

The graph below shows the average dry mass of the plants.

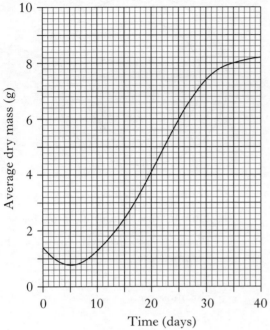

During which 5 day period is there the greatest increase in average dry mass?

A   Days   5 – 10

B   Days   10 – 15

C   Days   20 – 25

D   Days   25 – 30

9. The table below shows the results of an investigation into the effect of temperature on the number of eggs laid by female red spider mites.

	Temperature (°C)	
	20°C	30°C
Average number of eggs laid per female	90	60

The percentage decrease in the average number of eggs laid per female when the temperature is increased from 20°C to 30°C is

A   30%

B   33%

C   50%

D   67%.

10. A choice chamber was used to investigate the effect of humidity on the behaviour of woodlice, as shown below.

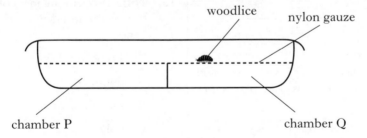

Which line in the table below describes the most appropriate set up for this investigation?

	Number of woodlice	Contents of chamber P	Contents of chamber Q	Modification to choice chamber
A	2	Drying agent	Wet cotton wool	Half covered in black paper
B	2	Wet cotton wool	Drying agent	Totally covered in black paper
C	10	Drying agent	Wet cotton wool	Half covered in black paper
D	10	Wet cotton wool	Drying agent	Totally covered in black paper

11. In corn on the cob, yellow seed (G) is dominant to purple seed (g). The cob shown below shows some yellow and some purple seeds. The seeds have been counted.

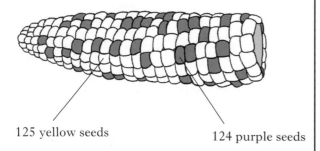

125 yellow seeds   124 purple seeds

The genotypes of the parents that produced this cob were

A   GG × gg

B   Gg × gg

C   gg × gg

D   Gg × Gg.

12. The table below shows the relationship between planting density and the mass of seed harvested for a trial cereal crop.

Planting density (number of plants per square metre)	Mass of seed harvested (grammes per square metre)
4	60
8	86
15	105
32	77
128	21

The reason a low mass of seed was harvested when the planting density was 128 plants per square metre was

A   less disease at high planting densities

B   more nutrients available

C   more competition for light and nutrients

D   less space for weeds.

13. Which stage in the production of human insulin by genetic engineering is represented in the diagram below?

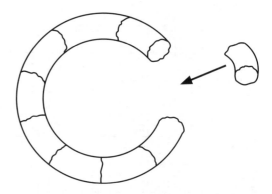

A   Human gene is inserted into a plasmid.

B   Human gene is inserted into a bacterium.

C   Plasmid is inserted into a human chromosome.

D   Bacterial gene is inserted into a human chromosome.

14. A hairy stemmed pea plant is crossed with a smooth stemmed pea plant. All the F₁ plants had hairy stems.

The genotype of the F₁ plants was

A   heterozygous

B   homozygous

C   dominant

D   recessive.

15. Differences in the mass of sunflower seeds are due to the interaction of the alleles of several genes.

This type of inheritance is called

A   dominant

B   monohybrid

C   polygenic

D   co-dominant.

16. Two groups of the seeds of genetically tall plants were grown under different conditions.

Group I seeds were grown in high light intensity and high nutrient levels.

Group II seeds were grown in low light intensity and low nutrient levels.

All plants in group I were taller than those in group II.

The effect of the different conditions on the phenotype is due to

A   natural selection

B   biodiversity

C   environmental impact

D   polygenic inheritance.

17. Which of the following is an example of selective breeding?

A   Increasing milk yield in dairy cattle

B   Industrial melanism in Peppered moths

C   Insulin production by bacteria

D   Insertion of DNA into a bacterium

18. Eight visking tubing (model gut) bags, as shown below, were placed into water baths.

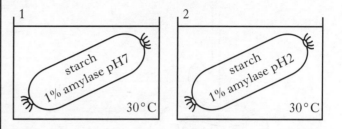

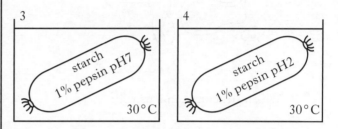

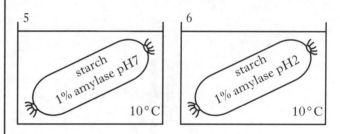

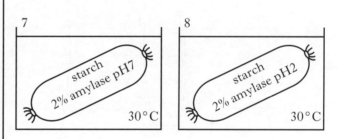

Which two bags could be compared to investigate the effect of pH on the digestion of starch?

A   1 and 4

B   2 and 5

C   2 and 7

D   7 and 8

[Turn over

19. The diagram below shows the human alimentary canal.

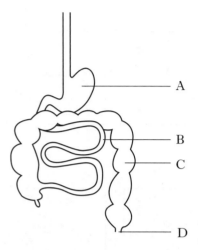

Which structure contains villi?

20. The diagram below shows the human urinary system.

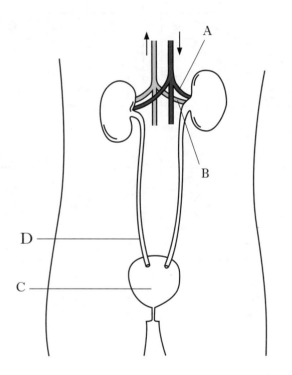

Which labelled part has the lowest concentration of urea?

21. A student has a heart rate of 80 beats per minute and a cardiac output of 4 litres per minute.

Cardiac output is calculated using the following equation:

Cardiac output = volume of blood × heart rate per beat

What is the volume of blood pumped per beat?

A $5\,cm^3$

B $20\,cm^3$

C $50\,cm^3$

D $320\,cm^3$

22. The diagram below shows the heart and circulation.

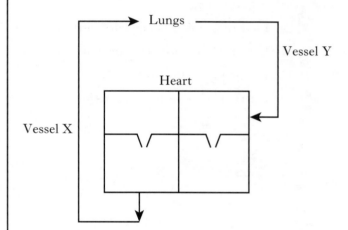

Which line in the table describes correctly the types of blood in vessels X and Y?

	Vessel X	Vessel Y
A	deoxygenated	deoxygenated
B	oxygenated	deoxygenated
C	oxygenated	oxygenated
D	deoxygenated	oxygenated

23. The list below refers to stages in the response of the nervous system to a stimulus.

1   Central nervous system sorts information.

2   Nerve impulses sent to muscles.

3   Nerve impulses sent to central nervous system.

4   Senses detect the stimulus.

5   Response is produced.

The correct order of the stages is

A $4 \rightarrow 3 \rightarrow 1 \rightarrow 2 \rightarrow 5$

B $3 \rightarrow 4 \rightarrow 2 \rightarrow 1 \rightarrow 5$

C $4 \rightarrow 3 \rightarrow 2 \rightarrow 1 \rightarrow 5$

D $3 \rightarrow 4 \rightarrow 1 \rightarrow 2 \rightarrow 5$.

24. The graph below shows the rates of water loss from an athlete when active and resting at different room temperatures.

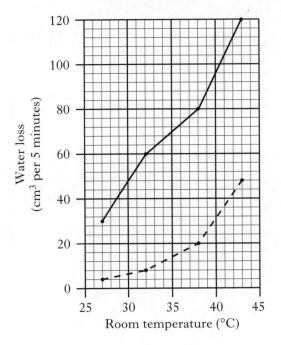

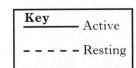

What is the difference in water loss per 5 minutes between active and resting at 43 °C?

A $70 \, cm^3$

B $72 \, cm^3$

C $76 \, cm^3$

D $78 \, cm^3$

25. Which of the following pathways shows the correct response in blood vessels of the skin to an increase in body temperature?

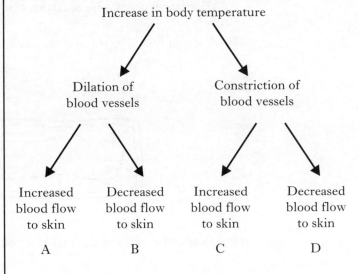

Candidates are reminded that the answer sheet for Section A MUST be placed INSIDE the front cover of this answer book.

Marks

SECTION B

All questions in this section should be attempted.
All answers must be written clearly and legibly in ink.

1. (*a*) The diagram below represents a potato cell.

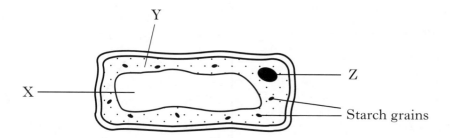

   (i) Name the parts of the cell labelled X and Y.

   X _____

   Y _____   **1**

   (ii) Give the function of structure Z.

   _____   **1**

   (*b*) Name the enzyme involved in the synthesis of starch in potato cells.

   _____   **1**

   (*c*) Give **one** difference and **one** similarity in the structure of plant and animal cells.

   Difference _____

   _____   **1**

   Similarity _____

   _____   **1**

Marks

2. (a) Yeast cells have many industrial and commercial uses.

The sentences below describe some of the uses of yeast cells.

<u>Underline</u> **one** option in each set of brackets to make the following sentences correct.

Yeast cells are $\left\{ \begin{array}{l} \text{bacteria} \\ \text{fungi} \end{array} \right\}$ that produce $\left\{ \begin{array}{l} \text{carbon dioxide} \\ \text{oxygen} \end{array} \right\}$ which makes bread

rise. Yeast cells are also used in the production of $\left\{ \begin{array}{l} \text{biogas} \\ \text{gasohol} \end{array} \right\}$.

2

(b) Explain how milk is converted into yoghurt by bacteria.

_____

_____

_____

2

[Turn over

Marks

3. An investigation was carried out to find the effect of salt solutions of different concentrations on the mass of potato tissue. Five test tubes were set up as shown below, each containing a different concentration of salt solution.

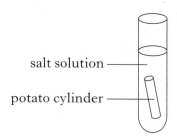

salt solution

potato cylinder

Each potato cylinder was weighed, placed in the solution and left for an hour. Each cylinder was then reweighed and the percentage (%) change in mass was calculated.

The table below shows the results of the investigation.

Salt concentration (g/100 cm³)	Change in mass (%)
1	+15
3	+10
6	−5
8	−15
10	−20

(a) (i) Add the appropriate label to each axis. 　　1

(ii) Construct a **line graph** using the results given in the table. 　　1

(Additional graph paper, if required, will be found on *Page thirty*.)

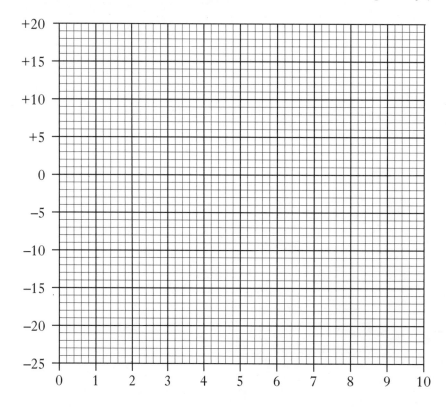

Marks

3.   **(continued)**

(*b*)   Time was kept constant in this investigation.

Name **two** other variables which must be kept constant.

1 _____

2 _____   1

(*c*)   Using the results given, state the salt concentration which is isotonic to the potato tissue. Explain your answer.

Isotonic concentration _____ g/100 cm^3 1

Explanation _____

_____   1

(*d*)   Predict the salt concentration that would produce a 10% decrease in mass.

_____ g/100 cm^3 1

[Turn over

Marks

4. Enzymes are biological catalysts. The diagram below shows part of an enzyme controlled reaction.

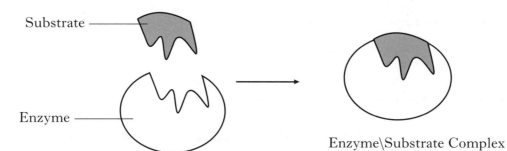

Substrate

Enzyme

Enzyme\Substrate Complex

(a) Describe the features of an enzyme which allow it to combine with only one substrate.

_____

_____

_____   2

(b) What happens to an enzyme when it is boiled?

_____   1

(c) Name a factor, other than temperature, which affects enzyme activity.

_____   1

(d) Complete the following word equation for the enzyme catalase.

                                  catalase

hydrogen peroxide $\longrightarrow$ _____ and _____   1

      substrate   **products**

Marks

5.   A study has shown that Scotland's river otter population is increasing after falling sharply over the last 40 years.

Otters live along the banks of rivers, usually in reeds and gaps between tree roots. Fish are their main food.

(*a*)   What term is used for the place where otters live?

_____

1

(*b*)   What disadvantage might otters have if reeds are removed from riverbanks?

_____

_____

1

(*c*)   Mink are North American animals introduced into Scotland. They feed on fish and live in riverbanks.

What effect would the mink have on otter numbers? Explain your answer.

Effect _____

Explanation _____

_____

2

(*d*)   An ecosystem such as the otters' has several components.

Complete the table below to identify the terms used and their definitions.

Term	Definition
	A green plant that makes its own food.
Carnivore	
Community	

2

Marks

6. Boll weevil insects, shown in the picture below, feed on cotton plants. There are two varieties of cotton plant, original variety (V) and boll weevil resistant variety (R).

Three farms were used to compare the yield of the two varieties. Each farmer planted two fields, one of each variety. All fields were treated identically. The yield of cotton from each field was weighed. The results are shown in the bar graph below.

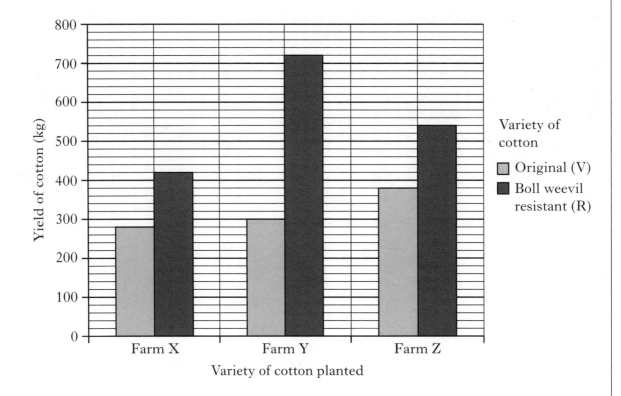

(*a*) Calculate the average yield of V cotton.

Space for calculation

_____ kg   **1**

Marks

6. **(continued)**

(*b*) Calculate the percentage difference in yield between the two varieties of cotton grown at Farm X.

Space for calculation

_____ %   1

(*c*) (i) Name the variable altered in this investigation.

_____   1

(ii) The fields planted with V cotton were used as a control.

Give a reason for using this control.

_____

_____   1

(iii) Explain why using ten farms instead of three would have improved this investigation.

_____   1

(*d*) What conclusion can be drawn from these results?

_____

_____   1

(*e*) The farmers use pesticides to kill insects which damage their crops.

(i) Explain why less pesticide is needed when growing R cotton.

_____

_____   1

(ii) Explain why growing R cotton is less likely to affect insect biodiversity.

_____

_____   1

[Turn over

Marks

7. (*a*) Hair appearance in mice is controlled by a single gene.

Wavy hair (H) is dominant to straight hair (h).

Two homozygous mice were crossed, one had wavy hair and one had straight hair.

(i) Complete the genotypes of the parental generation (P).

$$\textbf{Wavy haired} \quad \times \quad \textbf{Straight haired}$$

P genotypes _____ × _____   1

(ii) State the phenotype of the F_1 mice.

F_1 phenotype _____   1

(iii) An F_1 mouse was crossed with a straight haired mouse.

State the genotype of the wavy haired offspring.
Space for working

Genotype _____   1

(*b*) What term is used to describe alleles which are neither dominant nor recessive?

_____   1

(*c*) The sentence below describes the function of DNA.

<u>Underline</u> **one** option in each set of brackets to make the following sentence correct.

The $\left\{ \begin{array}{l} \text{number} \\ \text{order} \end{array} \right\}$ of DNA $\left\{ \begin{array}{l} \text{bases} \\ \text{genes} \end{array} \right\}$ in a chromosome encodes information

for the structure of a $\left\{ \begin{array}{l} \text{carbohydrate} \\ \text{protein} \end{array} \right\}$.   2

Marks

8. (*a*) Name **two** places in the alimentary canal where protein is digested.

1 _____

2 _____ **2**

(*b*) The nutrition information panel below is from a chocolate bar.

Each bar contains . . .			
Calories	**Sugars**	**Fat**	**Saturates**
170	17·7 g	9·9 g	6·6 g
8·5%	19·6%	14·1%	10·4%
of your guideline daily amount			

(i) According to this information, how many calories make up your guideline daily amount?

Space for calculation

_____ calories **1**

(ii) Saturates are a type of fat which form part of the total fat (9·9 g) in this chocolate bar.

What percentage of the total fat is saturates?

Space for calculation

_____% **1**

[Turn over

Marks

9. The diagram below shows an investigation into the effect of pH on the digestion of protein by trypsin.

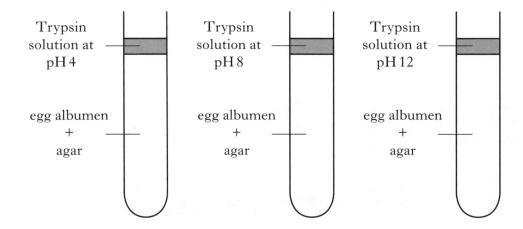

Egg albumen is the source of protein. It is added to agar to give a cloudy, white jelly. When the egg albumen is digested the jelly turns clear.

The test tubes were left in a warm place for 24 hours. At the end of this time the depth of the clear jelly was measured.

The graph below shows results from this investigation.

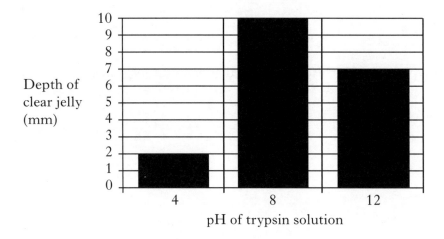

(a) Describe trypsin activity as pH increases as shown in the graph.

_____

_____

_____   2

Marks

9.   **(continued)**

(*b*)   Predict the depth of clear jelly with trypsin at pH 2.

————————— mm   **1**

(*c*)   Trypsin is produced by the pancreas. Name **two** other enzymes produced by the pancreas.

1 _____   **1**

2 _____   **1**

[Turn over

Marks

10. (*a*) Marine bony fish are found in the North Sea.

Underline **one** option in each set of brackets to make the following sentences correct.

Marine bony fish have tissues that are $\left\{ \begin{array}{c} \text{hypertonic} \\ \text{hypotonic} \end{array} \right\}$ to sea water.

They overcome osmotic problems by $\left\{ \begin{array}{c} \text{absorbing} \\ \text{excreting} \end{array} \right\}$ salts and producing

$\left\{ \begin{array}{c} \text{concentrated} \\ \text{dilute} \end{array} \right\}$ urine.   2

(*b*) The diagram below shows part of a nephron from a human kidney.

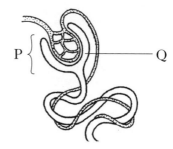

  (i) Name structure Q.

   _____   1

  (ii) Name the process carried out at P.

   _____   1

(*c*) The hormone ADH affects water reabsorption from the nephron.

  (i) Which part of the brain releases ADH?

   _____   1

  (ii) Name a part of a nephron where water is reabsorbed.

   _____   1

Marks

11. The diagram below shows an alveolus and a capillary in the lungs where gas exchange occurs.

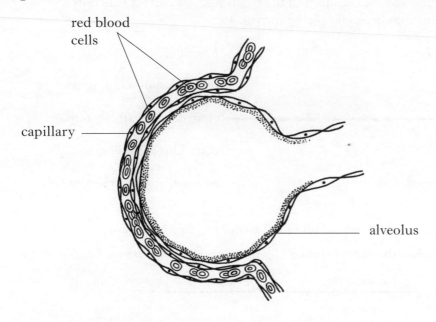

red blood cells

capillary

alveolus

(a) Decide if each of the following statements about gas exchange is **True** or **False**, and tick (✓) the appropriate box.

If the statement is **False**, write the correct word(s) in the **Correction** box to replace the word underlined in the statement.

Statement	True	False	Correction
Lungs have a <u>large</u> surface area for efficient gas exchange.			
The thin walls of alveoli <u>slow down</u> gas exchange.			
There is a lower <u>oxygen</u> concentration in the alveoli than in the blood.			

3

(b) How is oxygen carried in the red blood cells?

_____ 1

(c) Blood plasma transports the blood cells.

Name **two** other substances carried by the blood plasma.

_____ and _____ 1

[Turn over

Marks

12. (*a*) Different parts of the brain have different functions.

Draw **one** line to link each part of the brain with its correct function.
(One example has been completed for you.)

Part of the brain   *Function*

Cerebrum   regulation of temperature

Medulla ————————————————— control of breathing rate

Cerebellum   conscious responses

Hypothalamus   co-ordination of movement   2

(*b*) (i) The flow chart below shows the structures in a reflex arc.

Complete the chart by inserting the names of the missing neurones.

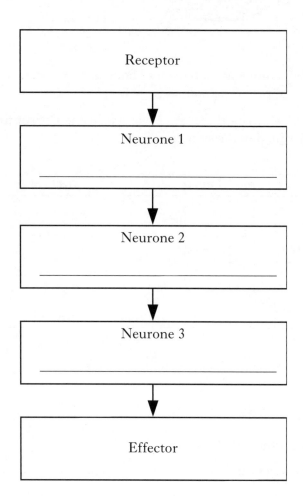

(ii) Describe a function of a reflex response.

_____

_____   1

[Turn over for Section C on *Page twenty-six*

SECTION C

Marks

Both questions in this section should be attempted.

Note that each question contains a choice.

**Questions 1 and 2 should be attempted on the blank pages which follow.
All answers must be written clearly and legibly in ink.**

Supplementary sheets, if required, may be obtained from the Invigilator.

1. Answer **either** A **or** B.

    A. The pictures below show a food chain which is also represented by two types of pyramid.

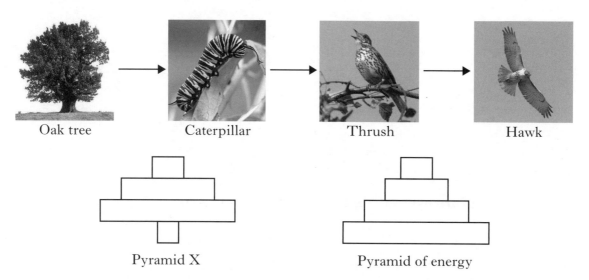

Oak tree	Caterpillar	Thrush	Hawk

Pyramid X   Pyramid of energy

Name the type of pyramid X. Explain why **both** pyramids are correct for this food chain.

5

OR

    B. The diagram below represents some of the stages of meiosis in the testes.

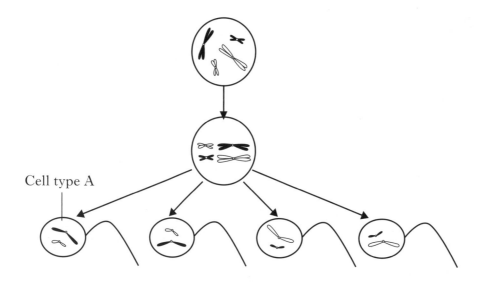

Cell type A

Name cell type A **and** describe the role of **both** meiosis and fertilisation in producing offspring.

5

Question 2 is on *Page twenty-eight*.

SPACE FOR ANSWER TO QUESTION 1

[Turn over for Question 2 on *Page twenty-eight*

Marks

2. Answer **either** A **or** B.

    Labelled diagrams may be included where appropriate.

    A. Describe the **two** stages of aerobic respiration **including** the names of the raw materials and products for **each** stage.   **5**

    OR

    B. Describe the **two** stages of photosynthesis **including** the names of the raw materials and products for **each** stage.   **5**

[END OF QUESTION PAPER]

SPACE FOR ANSWER TO QUESTION 2

ADDITIONAL SPACE FOR ANSWERS

ADDITIONAL GRAPH PAPER FOR QUESTION 3(*a*)

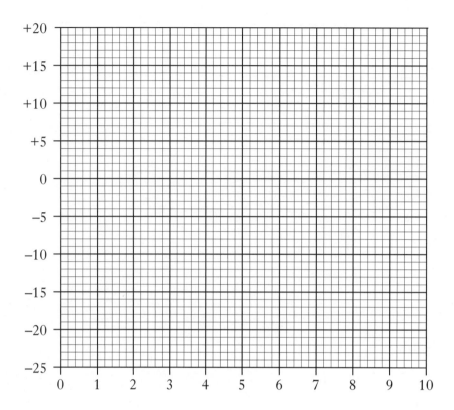

INTERMEDIATE 2

2012

[BLANK PAGE]

FOR OFFICIAL USE

Total for
Sections B and C

X007/11/02

NATIONAL
QUALIFICATIONS
2012

WEDNESDAY, 23 MAY
9.00 AM – 11.00 AM

BIOLOGY
INTERMEDIATE 2

Fill in these boxes and read what is printed below.

Full name of centre

Town

Forename(s)

Surname

Date of birth

Day   Month   Year   Scottish candidate number   Number of seat

SECTION A (25 marks)

Instructions for completion of Section A are given on *Page two*.

For this section of the examination you must use an HB pencil.

SECTIONS B AND C (75 marks)

1 (a) All questions should be attempted.

   (b) It should be noted that in **Section C** questions 1 and 2 each contain a choice.

2 The questions may be answered in any order but all answers are to be written in the spaces provided in this answer book, **and must be written clearly and legibly in ink**.

3 Additional space for answers will be found at the end of the book. If further space is required, supplementary sheets may be obtained from the Invigilator and should be inserted inside the **front** cover of this book.

4 The numbers of questions must be clearly inserted with any answers written in the additional space.

5 Rough work, if any should be necessary, should be written in this book and then scored through when the fair copy has been written. If further space is required, a supplementary sheet for rough work may be obtained from the Invigilator.

6 Before leaving the examination room you must give this book to the Invigilator. If you do not, you may lose all the marks for this paper.

Read carefully

1   Check that the answer sheet provided is for **Biology Intermediate 2 (Section A)**.

2   For this section of the examination you must use an **HB pencil**, and where necessary, an eraser.

3   Check that the answer sheet you have been given has **your name**, **date of birth**, **SCN** (Scottish Candidate Number) and **Centre Name** printed on it.

Do not change any of these details.

4   If any of this information is wrong, tell the Invigilator immediately.

5   If this information is correct, **print** your name and seat number in the boxes provided.

6   The answer to each question is **either** A, B, C or D. Decide what your answer is, then, using your pencil, put a horizontal line in the space provided (see sample question below).

7   There is **only one correct** answer to each question.

8   Any rough working should be done on the question paper or the rough working sheet, **not** on your answer sheet.

9   At the end of the examination, put the **answer sheet for Section A inside the front cover of this answer book**.

Sample Question

The thigh bone is called the

A   femur

B   humerus

C   tibia

D   fibula.

The correct answer is **A**—femur. The answer **A** has been clearly marked in **pencil** with a horizontal line (see below).

Changing an answer

If you decide to change your answer, carefully erase your first answer and, using your pencil, fill in the answer you want. The answer below has been changed to **D**.

SECTION A

All questions in this Section should be attempted.

Questions 1 and 2 refer to the plant cell diagram below.

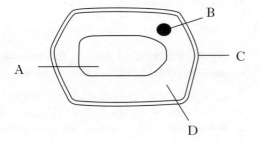

1. Which of the plant cell components shown above is made from a structural carbohydrate?

2. Which labelled part controls cell activities?

3. Which line in the table below shows what happens to cells when placed in a hypertonic solution?

	Animal Cell	Plant Cell
A	swells and bursts	becomes turgid
B	becomes turgid	swells and bursts
C	shrinks	becomes plasmolysed
D	becomes plasmolysed	becomes plasmolysed

4. The bar chart below shows the number of cells of different lengths in a sample of onion epidermis.

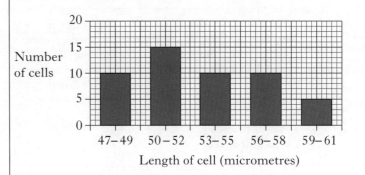

The percentage of cells with a length greater than 55 micrometres is

A　10%

B　15%

C　20%

D　30%.

5. The apparatus below was used to investigate gas exchange in germinating peas.

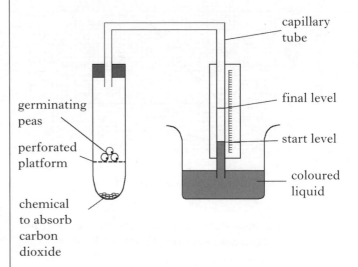

The movement of the coloured liquid in the capillary tube can be used to measure the volume of

A　oxygen produced by respiration

B　carbon dioxide used up by respiration

C　oxygen used up by respiration

D　carbon dioxide produced by respiration.

6. Which line in the table below correctly shows the functions of an enzyme?

	Energy input of the chemical reaction	Rate of the chemical reaction
A	lowers	speeds up
B	raises	slows down
C	raises	speeds up
D	lowers	slows down

7. Fungi produce

A   antibodies to destroy bacteria

B   antibiotics to engulf bacteria

C   antibiotics to destroy bacteria

D   antibodies to digest bacteria.

8. The graph below shows the effect of temperature on the activity of an enzyme.

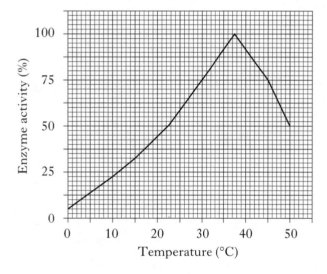

The increase in enzyme activity (%) as the temperature rises from 22·5 °C to 30 °C is

A   25

B   50

C   67

D   75.

9. The total variety of all living things on Earth is described as

A   an ecosystem

B   biodiversity

C   a community

D   random assortment.

10. A survey was carried out on the number of mussels attached to rocks on a seashore.

The positions of the mussels are shown by squares in the diagram below. The numbers of mussels at each position are shown in the squares.

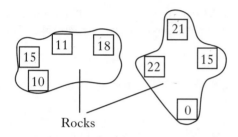

Rocks

What is the average number of mussels found per square?

A   14

B   16

C   56

D   112

11. The chart below shows the average height of trees in a woodland over a 25 year period.

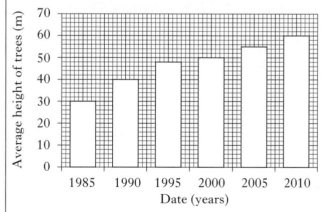

What is the percentage increase in tree height between 1985 and 2010?

A   30%

B   50%

C   60%

D   100%

12. Which of the following experiments could be used to show the response of an earthworm to temperature?

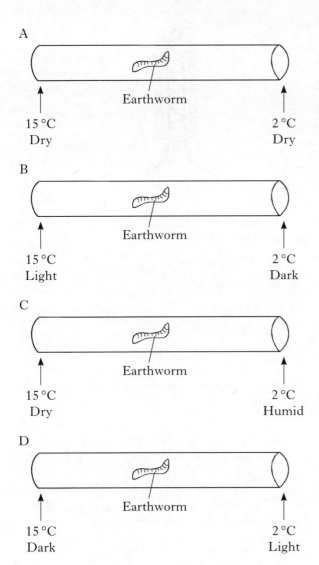

A

15 °C
Dry

2 °C
Dry

B

15 °C
Light

2 °C
Dark

C

15 °C
Dry

2 °C
Humid

D

15 °C
Dark

2 °C
Light

13. An organism has two different alleles of a gene.

This genotype is

A dominant

B homozygous

C recessive

D heterozygous.

14. *Distichiasis* is a dominant characteristic in humans which causes the person to have two rows of eyelashes.

A woman who is homozygous for the condition and a man who is unaffected have children.

What proportion of their children would be expected to have *Distichiasis*?

A 0%

B 25%

C 50%

D 100%

15. In dogs, uniform coat colour is dominant to spotted coat.

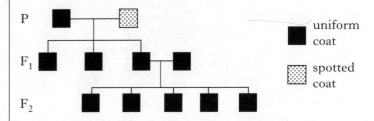

From the family tree above, in which generation(s) are all the dogs heterozygous for coat colour?

A P only

B F_1 only

C F_2 only

D P and F_1

16. In a breed of cattle, coat colour is determined by two alleles R and W. The possible genotypes are expressed as follows:

Genotype	Coat colour
RR	Red
RW	Roan
WW	White

Which term best describes the two alleles R and W?

A Heterozygous

B Co-dominant

C Homozygous

D Polygenic

17. The diagram below shows the human alimentary canal and its associated organs.

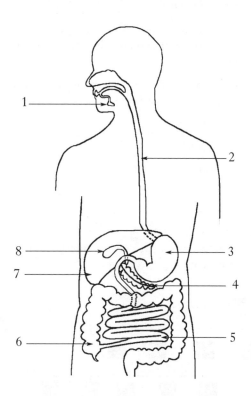

Which numbered parts produce digestive enzymes?

A 1, 2, 4

B 3, 4, 8

C 2, 7, 8

D 1, 3, 4

18. When different foods were burned, the following results were obtained.

Food	Temperature rise (°C)
Carbohydrate	15
Fat	40
Protein	20

Using the equation,

Energy value (kJ) = 4·2 × temperature rise (°C),

the energy value (kJ) of fat is

A 40

B 63

C 84

D 168.

19. The diagram below shows the structure of a villus.

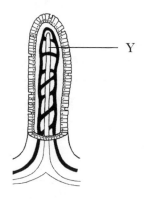

Which food molecules are absorbed by structure Y?

A Amino acids

B Fatty acids

C Glucose

D Glycogen

20. Excess protein in the diet is deaminated in the body.

Which line in the table below correctly describes the site of deamination and the waste product produced?

	Site of deamination	Waste product
A	liver	urea
B	kidney	urea
C	kidney	amino acids
D	liver	amino acids

21. The diagram below shows the heart and circulation.

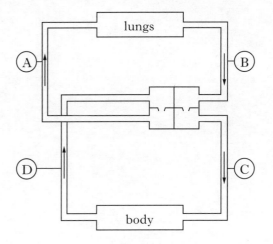

Which labelled structure is the pulmonary artery?

22. The table below shows water gained and lost by an individual over a 24 hour period.

Method of water gain	Volume of water gained (cm³)	Method of water loss	Volume of water lost (cm³)
food	850	exhaled breath	300
drink	1000	urine	1250
metabolic water		sweating	500
		faeces	100

The individual is in water balance over the 24 hour period.

What volume of water is gained as metabolic water?

A   100 cm³

B   200 cm³

C   300 cm³

D   500 cm³

23. A scientist investigated how the salt concentration of drinks affected urine production.

Volunteers were given drinks of different salt concentrations and their urine production was measured.

Which variable should be kept constant during this investigation?

A   Volume of drink given.

B   Volume of urine measured.

C   Concentration of salt in the drink.

D   Concentration of urine measured.

24. Marine bony fish have to overcome an osmoregulation problem.

Which line in the table is true for marine bony fish?

	Salt transport at gills	Volume of urine produced
A	absorbed	small
B	excreted	large
C	excreted	small
D	absorbed	large

[Turn over

25. The diagram below shows a cross section of a human heart.

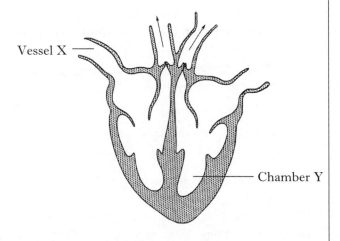

Vessel X

Chamber Y

Which line in the table identifies the parts of the heart correctly?

	Vessel X	Chamber Y
A	aorta	left ventricle
B	vena cava	left ventricle
C	vena cava	right ventricle
D	aorta	right ventricle

Candidates are reminded that the answer sheet for Section A MUST be placed INSIDE the front cover of this answer book.

[Turn over for Section B on *Page ten*

SECTION B

Marks

All questions in this Section should be attempted.
All answers must be written clearly and legibly in ink.

1. The diagrams below represent two industrial processes, Q and R.

   Each process uses a different type of cell for anaerobic respiration.

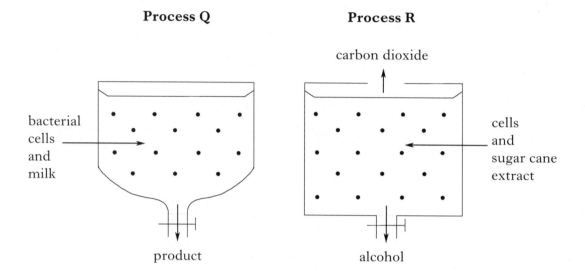

        Process Q   **Process R**

        product   alcohol

   (a) (i) Complete the following equation for Process Q.

$$\text{milk sugar (lactose)} \xrightarrow{\text{bacterial cells}} \underline{\hspace{5cm}}$$

   1

   (ii) The milk curdles and a product is made in Process Q.
        Name this product.

   _____

   1

   (b) (i) Name the cells used in Process R.

   _____

   1

   (ii) How is the alcohol from Process R used to fuel cars?

   _____

   _____   2

Marks

2. An investigation was carried out to find the effect of pH on the activity of an enzyme.

Substrate at different pH values was added to the enzyme in different test tubes.

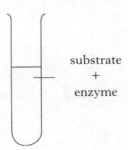

substrate
+
enzyme

(a) State **two** variables that must be kept constant for a valid conclusion to be made from this investigation.

1 _____

2 _____   2

(b) The results of this investigation are shown in the graph below.

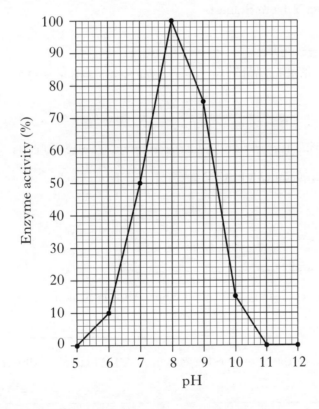

(i) What is the optimum pH for this enzyme?

_____   1

(ii) How many times more active is the enzyme at pH 9 than at pH 10?
Space for calculation

_____ times   1

Marks

3. The process of aerobic respiration in a muscle cell is outlined below.

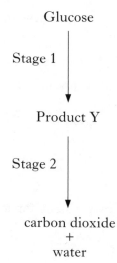

Glucose

Stage 1

Product Y

Stage 2

carbon dioxide
+
water

(*a*)　(i)　Name Stage 1.

_____   1

(ii)　Name product Y from Stage 1.

_____   1

(iii)　What other substance must be present for Stage 2 to occur?

_____   1

(*b*)　ATP is formed during respiration and broken down for uses in cells.

(i)　How many molecules of ATP are formed from each glucose molecule during

Stage 1 only?_____

Both Stage 1 and Stage 2? _____   1

(ii)　What **two** molecules are produced when ATP is broken down?

_____ and _____   1

(iii)　State **one** use of the energy released when ATP is broken down.

_____   1

Marks

4.   The following diagrams show an investigation into osmosis using four model cells.

The model cells were weighed before placing them in the test tubes.

After one hour the model cells were taken out of the test tubes and reweighed.

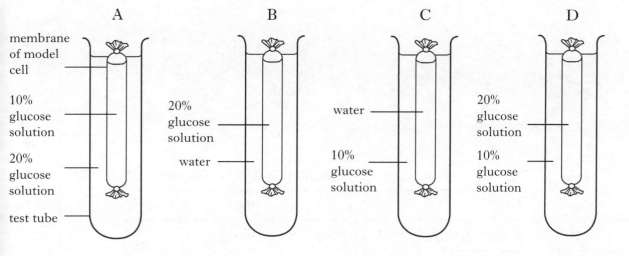

(a)   What feature of the membrane of the model cell makes it suitable for this investigation?

_____   1

(b)   State the letters of the model cells which would have increased in mass after one hour.

_____   1

(c)   What should be done to the model cells before each weighing to obtain valid results?

_____   1

(d)   Predict which model cell would have the greatest change in mass after one hour.

Give a reason for your choice.

Model cell _____   1

Reason _____

_____   1

[Turn over

Marks

5. (*a*) A student set up five petri dishes to investigate the effect of competition on the percentage of seedlings surviving after five days. Each dish contained a thin layer of wet cotton wool with different numbers of seeds placed evenly across its surface, as shown below.

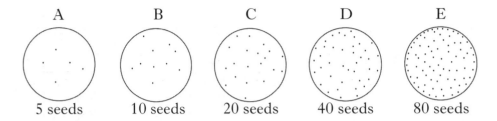

The table of results for this investigation is shown below.

Dish	*Number of seeds sown*	*Seedlings surviving after five days (%)*
A	5	100
B	10	100
C	20	95
D	40	85
E	80	75

(i) Construct a **line graph** to show the number of seeds sown against percentage of seedlings surviving after five days.

(Additional graph paper, if required, will be found on *Page twenty-eight*.)

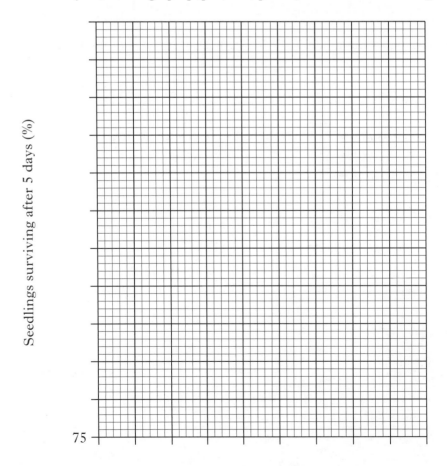

Seedlings surviving after 5 days (%)

75

Number of seeds sown

2

Marks

5. **(a)** **(continued)**

(ii)   Name the variable which is altered in this investigation.

_____   1

(iii)   What conclusion can be drawn from these results?

_____

_____   1

(iv)   Calculate the simple whole number ratio of the percentage of seedlings surviving in dish A compared to dish E.

Space for calculation

_____ : _____   1
Dish A   Dish E

(v)   Another dish was set up with 160 seeds and 88 seedlings survived for five days.

Calculate the percentage of seedlings surviving in this dish.

Space for calculation

_____ %   1

(b) Name **one** requirement, other than water, for which plants may be in competition.

_____   1

[Turn over

6. The diagram below represents a food web from a Scottish river ecosystem.

Marks

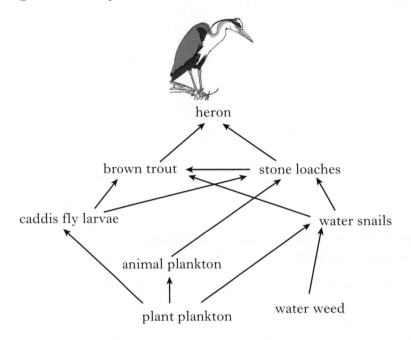

heron

brown trout ⟷ stone loaches

caddis fly larvae

water snails

animal plankton

plant plankton   water weed

(a) Decide if each of the following statements about this food web is **True** or **False**, and tick (✓) the appropriate box.

If the statement is **False**, write the correct word in the **Correction** box to replace the word underlined in the statement.

Statement	True	False	Correction
The stone loaches are the predators of the brown trout.			
There are three producers in this food web.			
The caddis fly larvae are herbivores.			

3

(b) (i) Complete the food chain below with four organisms from this food web.

water weed ⟶ _____ ⟶ _____ ⟶ _____ ⟶ _____

1

(ii) What do the arrows in the food chain represent?

_____

1

(c) A pyramid of biomass shows the mass of living organisms at each level. Explain why the heron has the lowest biomass in this food web.

_____

_____

_____

2

Marks

7. The diagram below represents some of the stages of genetic engineering which are used to produce medicines such as insulin for human use.

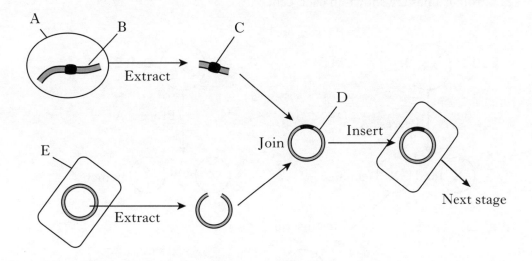

(a) Complete the table below to identify the labelled parts of the diagram.

Name of structure	Letter
bacterial cell	
insulin gene	
plasmid	

2

(b) Describe the next stage needed to produce insulin for use as a medicine.

_____

_____   1

(c) Name another human hormone produced by genetic engineering.

_____   1

(d) State **one** advantage of genetic engineering.

_____

_____   1

[Turn over

Marks

8. The diagram below represents some of the processes involved in human reproduction.

   The sex chromosomes are shown in each cell.

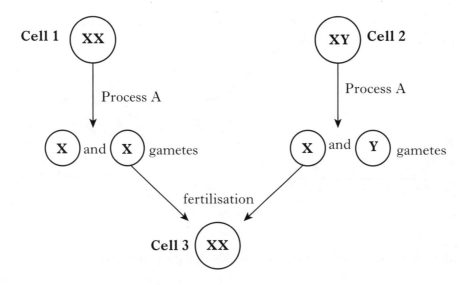

   (*a*) Which cell(s) are female?

   Circle the correct cell(s) below.

   Cell 1 / Cell 2 / Cell 3   1

   (*b*) (i) Name process A which forms gametes.

   _____   1

   (ii) Explain what happens to the chromosomes during process A.

   _____

   _____

   _____

   _____   2

   (*c*) Underline **one** option in each set of brackets to make the following sentence about fertilisation correct.

   Cell 3 is a $\begin{Bmatrix} \text{body cell} \\ \text{zygote} \end{Bmatrix}$ formed when the $\begin{Bmatrix} \text{cytoplasm} \\ \text{nuclei} \end{Bmatrix}$ of the two gametes

   $\begin{Bmatrix} \text{divide} \\ \text{fuse} \end{Bmatrix}$ at fertilisation.   2

Marks

9. (*a*) Blood contains plasma and cells which are used for transport and in defence.

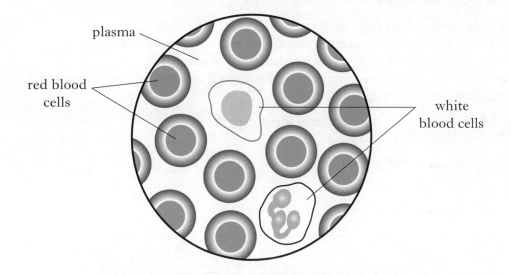

    (i) Name the type of white blood cell that can produce antibodies.

_____   1

    (ii) Carbon dioxide is carried in blood plasma. Name the other part of the blood that also carries carbon dioxide.

_____   1

    (iii) Name the chemical formed in red blood cells at high oxygen levels in the lungs.

_____   1

(*b*) The table below shows how altitude affects the percentage oxygen carried in blood.

Altitude (metres)	*Percentage oxygen carried in blood* (%)
(sea level) 0	97
2800	91
3700	85
4700	80

Use the data in the table to explain why a runner who lives at an altitude of 2800 metres would fatigue more quickly if racing in an event at 4700 metres.

_____

_____

_____   2

Marks

10. An investigation was carried out to study the effect of physical training on recovery time.

   The investigation was carried out as described below.

   - Twenty students did an exercise test.
   - Their heart rates were recorded before, during and after the exercise test.
   - The students then did a training programme for 8 weeks.
   - At the end of the training programme, the twenty students repeated the exercise test.
   - Average heart rates were calculated.

   The graph below shows the results of this investigation.

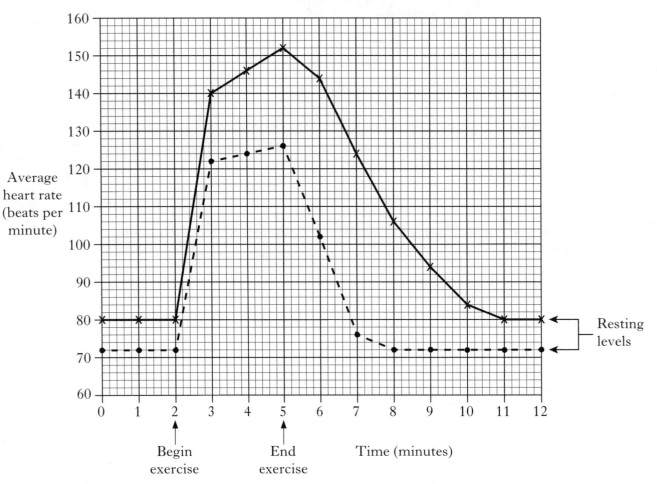

   Recovery time is the length of time taken for heart rate to return to resting level after exercise.

   (a) How long was the recovery time before the training programme?

   _____ minutes   1

DO NOT WRITE IN THIS MARGIN

Marks

10. (continued)

(*b*) (i) What was the percentage increase in average heart rate during the first minute of exercise before the training programme?

Space for calculation

____________ % **1**

(ii) What was the highest average heart rate during the exercise test for the students after the training programme?

____________ beats per minute **1**

(*c*) What feature of this investigation helped to improve the reliability of the results?

____ **1**

[Turn over

Marks

11. The diagram below shows some structures of the human lungs.

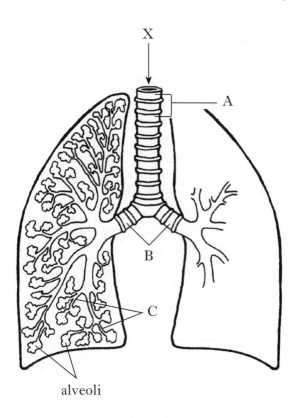

(a) Complete the following flow chart to give the pathway of air from X to the alveoli by inserting the names of the structures labelled in the diagram.

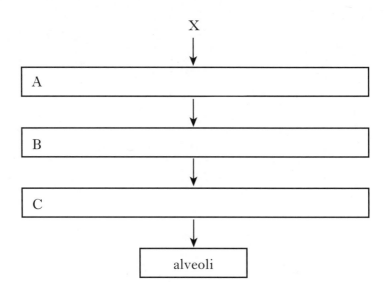

2

(b) (i) Name the process by which oxygen moves from the lungs into the blood.

_____ 1

(ii) State **two** features of alveoli which allow efficient gas exchange.

1 _____

2 _____ 2

Marks

12. (*a*) The diagram below shows the structures found in a reflex arc.

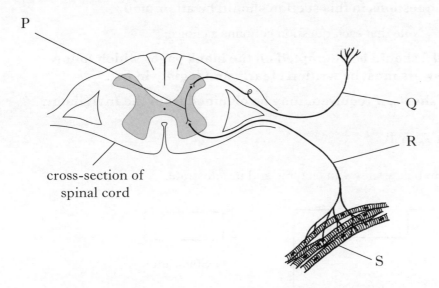

cross-section of
spinal cord

Complete the table below to identify the structures and their functions.

Structure	Letter	Function
Sensory neurone		Carries impulses from the receptor to the spinal cord
	P	Passes impulses from the sensory neurone to the motor neurone
Effector		

3

(*b*) The sentences below give the functions of some parts of the central nervous system.

Underline **one** option in each set of brackets to make the sentences correct.

The $\begin{Bmatrix} \text{medulla} \\ \text{spinal cord} \end{Bmatrix}$ controls the breathing rate and the $\begin{Bmatrix} \text{cerebellum} \\ \text{cerebrum} \end{Bmatrix}$

coordinates movements of the body.

A change in the water concentration of the blood is detected by the

$\begin{Bmatrix} \text{hypothalamus} \\ \text{pituitary gland} \end{Bmatrix}$.

2

(*c*) Name the hormone which is released to control reabsorption of water in the kidney.

_____

1

[Turn over for Section C on *Page twenty-four*

Marks

SECTION C

Both questions in this section should be attempted.

Note that each question contains a choice.

**Questions 1 and 2 should be attempted on the blank pages which follow.
All answers must be written clearly and legibly in ink.**

Supplementary sheets, if required, may be obtained from the Invigilator.

1. Answer **either** A **or** B.

   A.   The diagram below shows an enzyme and its substrate.

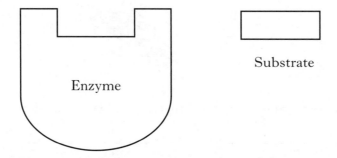

   Using a **named example**, describe what happens to this enzyme and its substrate during a **degradation** reaction.

5

   OR

   B.   The diagram below shows the green water plant *Elodea* used in an experiment to investigate photosynthesis.

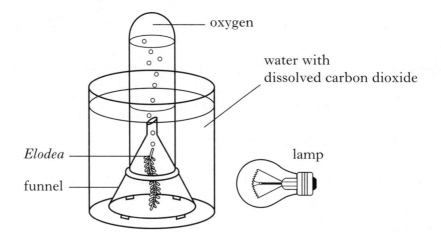

   Describe how the requirements for photosynthesis shown in the diagram are used in photolysis and carbon fixation to produce oxygen and starch.

5

Question 2 is on *Page twenty-six*.

DO NOT
WRITE
IN THIS
MARGIN

Marks

SPACE FOR ANSWER TO QUESTION 1

[Turn over for Question 2 on *Page twenty-six*

Marks

2. Answer **either** A **or** B.

   Labelled diagrams may be included where appropriate.

   A. The stomach wall contains muscles and cells that produce acid and mucus.

   Explain the functions of these muscles and cells in digestion.   **5**

   OR

   B. The human body can detect and respond to an increase in body temperature. Explain how the brain and the skin are involved in returning the body temperature to normal.   **5**

   [END OF QUESTION PAPER]

SPACE FOR ANSWER TO QUESTION 2

ADDITIONAL SPACE FOR ANSWERS

ADDITIONAL GRAPH PAPER FOR QUESTION 5(*a*)(i)

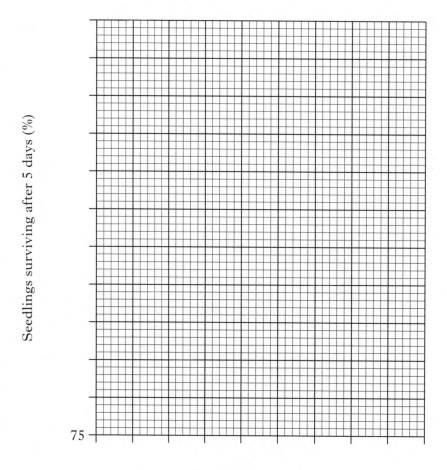

ADDITIONAL SPACE FOR ANSWERS

ADDITIONAL SPACE FOR ANSWERS

[BLANK PAGE]

FOR OFFICIAL USE

Total for
Sections B and C

X007/11/02

NATIONAL
QUALIFICATIONS
2013

WEDNESDAY, 15 MAY
9.00 AM – 11.00 AM

BIOLOGY
INTERMEDIATE 2

Fill in these boxes and read what is printed below.

Full name of centre

Town

Forename(s)

Surname

Date of birth

Day	Month	Year	Scottish candidate number	Number of seat

SECTION A (25 marks)

Instructions for completion of Section A are given on *Page two*.

For this section of the examination you must use an HB pencil.

SECTIONS B AND C (75 marks)

1 (a) All questions should be attempted.

(b) It should be noted that in **Section C** questions 1 and 2 each contain a choice.

2 The questions may be answered in any order but all answers are to be written in the spaces provided in this answer book, **and must be written clearly and legibly in ink**.

3 Additional space for answers will be found at the end of the book. If further space is required, supplementary sheets may be obtained from the Invigilator and should be inserted inside the **front** cover of this book.

4 The numbers of questions must be clearly inserted with any answers written in the additional space.

5 Rough work, if any should be necessary, should be written in this book and then scored through when the fair copy has been written. If further space is required, a supplementary sheet for rough work may be obtained from the Invigilator.

6 Before leaving the examination room you must give this book to the Invigilator. If you do not, you may lose all the marks for this paper.

Read carefully

1   Check that the answer sheet provided is for **Biology Intermediate 2 (Section A)**.

2   For this section of the examination you must use an **HB pencil** and, where necessary, an eraser.

3   Check that the answer sheet you have been given has **your name**, **date of birth**, **SCN** (Scottish Candidate Number) and **Centre Name** printed on it.

    Do not change any of these details.

4   If any of this information is wrong, tell the Invigilator immediately.

5   If this information is correct, **print** your name and seat number in the boxes provided.

6   The answer to each question is **either** A, B, C or D. Decide what your answer is, then, using your pencil, put a horizontal line in the space provided (see sample question below).

7   There is **only one correct** answer to each question.

8   Any rough working should be done on the question paper or the rough working sheet, **not** on your answer sheet.

9   At the end of the examination, put the **answer sheet for Section A inside the front cover of this answer book**.

Sample Question

The thigh bone is called the

A   femur

B   humerus

C   tibia

D   fibula.

The correct answer is **A**—femur. The answer **A** has been clearly marked in **pencil** with a horizontal line (see below).

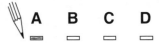

Changing an answer

If you decide to change your answer, carefully erase your first answer and, using your pencil, fill in the answer you want. The answer below has been changed to **D**.

A   B   C   D

SECTION A

All questions in this Section should be attempted.

1. Enzymes act as catalysts because they

   A   raise energy input

   B   lower energy input

   C   act on all substrates

   D   are composed of protein.

2. The diagram below represents a degradation reaction involving an enzyme.

   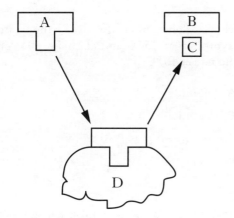

   Which letter identifies the substrate?

3. The enzyme phosphorylase was added to a 4% glucose-1-phosphate solution. After one hour, the concentration of glucose-1-phosphate had fallen to 0·1%.

   How many times lower was the concentration after one hour than at the start?

   A   97·5

   B   40·0

   C   3·9

   D   0·1

4. Which line in the table below correctly identifies the yield of ATP per glucose molecule in aerobic and anaerobic respiration?

	Number of ATP molecules	
	Aerobic respiration	Anaerobic respiration
A	2	18
B	2	38
C	18	2
D	38	2

5. Four reactions in the respiration pathway are shown below.

   1   Glucose → pyruvic acid

   2   Pyruvic acid → carbon dioxide + water

   3   Pyruvic acid → lactic acid

   4   Pyruvic acid → carbon dioxide + ethanol

   Which of the reactions can occur in yeast?

   A   2 and 3 only

   B   2 and 4 only

   C   1, 2 and 3 only

   D   1, 2 and 4 only

[Turn over

Questions 6 and 7 are based on the following information.

An investigation into anaerobic respiration in yeast was carried out.

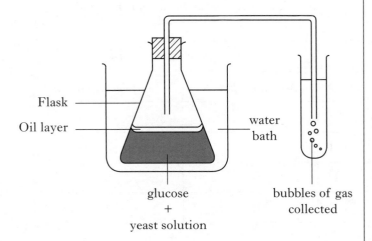

Flask

Oil layer

water bath

glucose
+
yeast solution

bubbles of gas collected

6. The purpose of the oil layer in the flask is to ensure that

A   oxygen from the solution is not released into the flask

B   carbon dioxide from the flask does not enter the solution

C   oxygen from the air does not enter the solution

D   carbon dioxide from the solution is not released into the flask.

7. A control flask was set up to show that anaerobic respiration is due to the activity of yeast. The solution in the control flask was

A   yeast and glucose

B   dead yeast and glucose

C   yeast and water

D   dead yeast and water.

8. The table below shows the rate of photosynthesis in a plant, at 10 °C and 15 °C, in different light intensities.

Light Intensity (units)	Rate of Photosynthesis	
	10 °C	15 °C
2	4	5
4	10	15
6	15	30
8	22	45

At which light intensity was the rate of photosynthesis at 15 °C found to be 50% greater than the rate at 10 °C?

A   2 units

B   4 units

C   6 units

D   8 units

9. The Treecreeper is a bird which feeds on small insects on the bark of trees during the day.

What is the correct description of the Treecreeper's niche?

A   The place where it lives

B   The insects on which it feeds

C   The plants and animals in the woodland environment

D   Its role within the woodland ecosystem

10. The graph below shows information about the height a bird feeds at and the length of its prey.

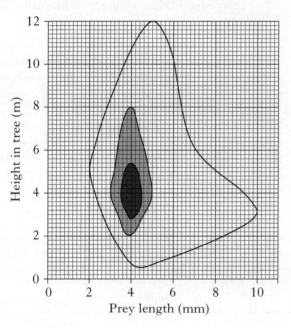

Key

Percentage of diet

 Greater than 5%

 3–5%

 1–3%

A correct conclusion would be that these birds eat most prey of length

A   4 mm

B   5 mm

C   10 mm

D   12 mm.

11. The diagram below shows the number of organisms at each level in a pyramid of numbers.

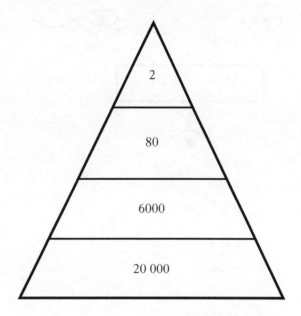

How many organisms are consumers?

A   2

B   82

C   6000

D   6082

12. The diagram below shows the feeding relationships of some of the organisms found in a fresh water loch.

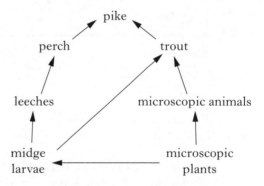

Which population of organisms in this food web would have the smallest biomass?

A   Pike

B   Trout

C   Microscopic animals

D   Microscopic plants

13. The diagram below shows the process of fertilisation.

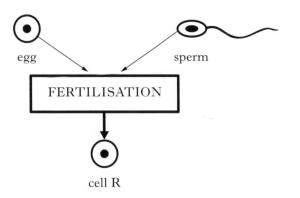

cell R

Cell R is

A   a zygote

B   a gamete

C   an ovule

D   an embryo.

14. The effects of 2 hormones, P and Q, on human sperm production are shown in the graph below.

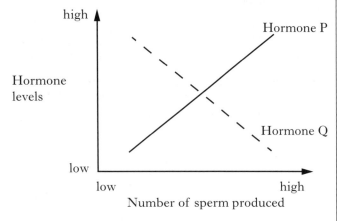

Number of sperm produced

A possible conclusion from the graph is that when the level of

A   hormone P is high and hormone Q is high, sperm production is low

B   hormone P is low and hormone Q is low, sperm production is low

C   hormone P is low and hormone Q is high, sperm production is high

D   hormone P is high and hormone Q is low, sperm production is high.

15. Methylene blue can be used to compare oxygen levels in water samples.

As oxygen levels decrease, the colour of methylene blue changes from blue to colourless.

The table below shows the appearance of methylene blue after being added to four water samples.

Water sample	Colour of Samples			
	Start	After 1 hour	After 3 days	After 5 days
A	blue	blue	blue	light blue
B	blue	blue	light blue	colourless
C	blue	light blue	colourless	colourless
D	blue	blue	blue	blue

One sample was collected below a sewage pipe.

Which sample is this most likely to be?

16. Which of the following crosses shows the effects of co-dominant genes?

	Parental phenotypes		Ratio of F₁ phenotypes
A	black fur mouse	× white fur mouse	1 black fur mouse : 1 white fur mouse
B	white flowered snapdragon	× red flowered snapdragon	all pink flowered snapdragons
C	pea plants with round seeds	× pea plants with wrinkled seeds	all pea plants with round seeds
D	smooth haired hamster	× smooth haired hamster	3 smooth haired hamsters : 1 rough haired hamster

17. Which of the following is a benefit of selective breeding in dairy cattle?

   A   Desired results are guaranteed.

   B   It leads to increased genetic variation.

   C   Increased yields can eventually be produced.

   D   Improvements are produced in one generation.

18. The table below shows some of the functions and sources of minerals.

Mineral	Function	Food sources
calcium	hardens bones and teeth; muscle contraction	milk, other dairy products, green vegetables
iron	component of haemoglobin and some enzymes	meat, nuts, cereals, green vegetables
sodium	transmission of nerve impulses; muscle contraction	meat, fish, salt
potassium	transmission of nerve impulses; muscle contraction	fish, meat, green vegetables

Which of the following minerals involved in contraction of muscles would be supplied by a meal of fish and green vegetables?

   A   Calcium and potassium only

   B   Iron, sodium and potassium only

   C   Calcium, sodium and potassium only

   D   Sodium and potassium only

19. The diagram below shows an investigation into the digestion of starch by amylase, using a model gut.

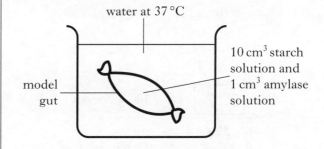

water at 37 °C

model gut

10 cm³ starch solution and 1 cm³ amylase solution

Which line in the table below describes correctly the content of a model gut which should be used as a control?

	Starch solution (cm³)	Amylase solution (cm³)	Water (cm³)
A	10	0	1
B	0	10	1
C	10	1	0
D	1	0	10

[Turn over

20. The diagram below shows the apparatus used to investigate the energy content of different foods.

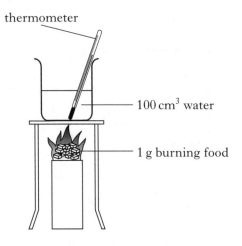

thermometer

100 cm³ water

1 g burning food

When different foods were burned, the following results were obtained.

Food	Temperature rise (°C)
potato	12
margarine	30
egg	15

The following equation can be used to calculate the energy value of food.

Energy value = 0·42 × temperature
(kJ per gram)   rise (°C)

Using this equation, the energy value of margarine is

A   1260

B   126

C   30·42

D   12·6.

21. Marine bony fish have to overcome an osmoregulation problem.

Which line in the table is correct for how marine bony fish overcome the problem?

	Salts	Concentration of urine produced
A	absorbed	concentrated
B	excreted	dilute
C	excreted	concentrated
D	absorbed	dilute

22. The diagram below shows the human alimentary canal.

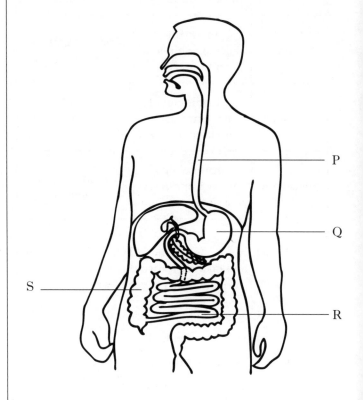

Peristalsis occurs in

A   P only

B   P and R only

C   P, R and S only

D   P, Q, R and S.

23. The diagram below shows the structure of the lungs.

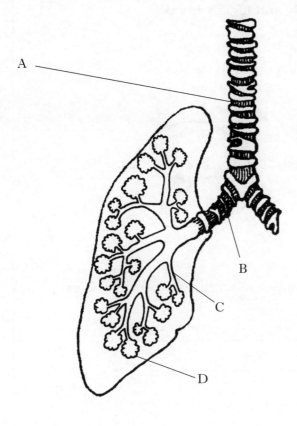

Which letter identifies a bronchiole?

24. The following diagram shows a human brain.

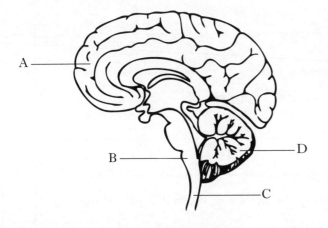

Which letter indicates the site of memory and conscious responses?

25. The diagram below shows neurones connecting the eye with the central nervous system.

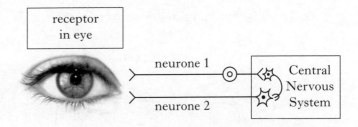

Which line in the table below identifies correctly the types of neurones and the direction of impulses which travel along them?

	Neurone 1	Neurone 2
A	Motor →	← Sensory
B	Sensory →	← Motor
C	← Motor	← Sensory
D	← Sensory	Motor →

Candidates are reminded that the answer sheet for Section A MUST be placed INSIDE the front cover of this answer book.

[**Turn over for Section B on *Page ten***

SECTION B

Marks

All questions in this Section should be attempted.
All answers must be written clearly and legibly in ink.

1. The diagrams below show two cells.

Plant cell Animal cell

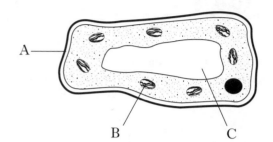
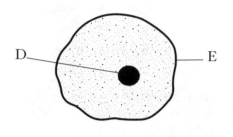

(*a*) Complete the table below to show the names and functions of some of these labelled parts.

Part	Name	Function
B	chloroplast	
C		contains cell sap
E	cell membrane	

2

(*b*) (i) The plant cell is placed in a hypertonic solution.

Describe the appearance of the plant cell after one hour.

_____

_____   1

(ii) Explain why the animal cell would stay the same size when it is placed in an isotonic solution.

_____

_____   2

Marks

2. (*a*) A nutrient agar plate was set up to find out the effect of one antibiotic on the growth of two different bacterial species. Two discs containing the same antibiotic were added, one to each half, as shown below.

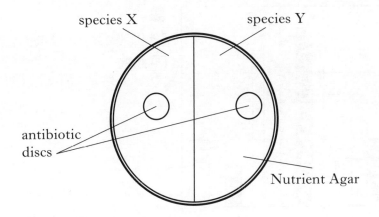

The plate was left in a warm place for 48 hours for the bacteria to grow on the nutrient agar. The results are shown below.

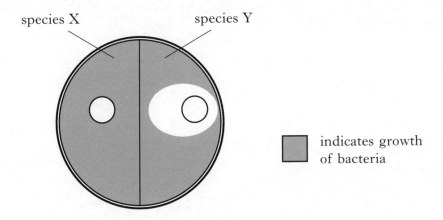

Which bacterial species is resistant to the antibiotic?

Give a reason for your answer.

Species _____   1

Reason _____

_____   1

(*b*) Antibiotic resistant bacteria are on the increase. Give a reason for this.

_____

_____   1

(*c*) Which type of organisms produce antibiotics?

_____   1

3. A student set up an investigation to measure the activity of catalase in a variety of foods at three different temperatures.

The bar graph below shows the results recorded by the student.

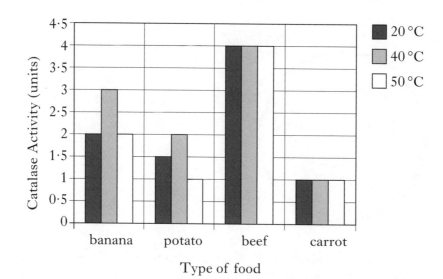

Marks

(a) Describe the changes in catalase activity in banana when the temperature increased from 20 °C to 50 °C.

_____

_____ 1

(b) Calculate the percentage decrease in catalase activity in potato when the temperature increased from 40 °C to 50 °C.

Space for calculation

_____ % 1

(c) Using the results for **banana and potato** only, state the temperature that gave the highest catalase activity.

_____ °C 1

(d) What conclusion can be drawn about catalase activity using the results for **carrots** only?

_____

_____ 1

(e) Predict the catalase activity in beef at 100 °C. Give a reason for your answer.

Prediction _____ units

Reason _____

_____ 1

Marks

4. (*a*)   A model cell was made using a visking tubing bag filled with a starch and amino acid solution. It was placed into a beaker of water and left for two hours.

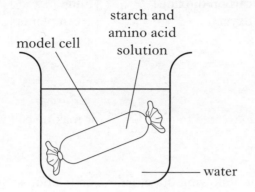

(i)   Amino acids were detected in the water outside the model cell.

What process is responsible for this movement?

_____   1

(ii)   Why would no starch be detected in the water outside the model cell?

_____

_____   1

(iii)   What would happen to the mass of the model cell during the two hour period? Explain your answer.

Mass of model cell _____

Explanation_____

_____   2

(*b*)   The diagram below represents a respiring liver cell carrying out deamination.

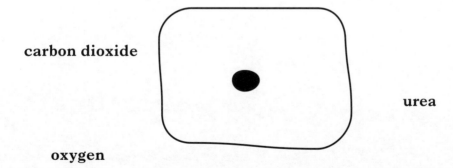

Complete the diagram above by adding **arrows** to show the direction of movement of urea, carbon dioxide and oxygen into or out of the cell.   2

[Turn over

Marks

5. (*a*) The sentences below give some information about photosynthesis.

Underline **one** option in each set of brackets to make the sentences correct.

Photosynthesis uses $\left\{\begin{array}{l}\text{carbon dioxide}\\\text{oxygen}\end{array}\right\}$ to allow $\left\{\begin{array}{l}\text{fungi}\\\text{green plants}\end{array}\right\}$ to make

their own food.

Some of this food is converted to $\left\{\begin{array}{l}\text{cellulose}\\\text{starch}\end{array}\right\}$ for making cell walls.

2

(*b*) Decide if each of the following statements about photosynthesis is **True** or **False**, and tick (✓) the appropriate box.

If the statement is **False**, write the correct word(s) in the **Correction** box to replace the word(s) underlined in the statement.

Statement	True	False	Correction
The first reaction in photosynthesis is called <u>carbon fixation</u>.			
<u>Hydrogen</u> is transferred from the first reaction to the second reaction.			
<u>ADP</u> is used as the energy source for the second reaction in photosynthesis.			

3

Marks

6. (a) The diagrams below give some information about three species of Darwin's Finches which live on the Galapagos Islands.

Feeds on insects   Feeds on seeds   Feeds on seeds

Using evidence from the diagrams, explain why these three finch species occupy different niches.

_____

_____

_____   2

(b) Some areas on the islands have a thin layer of soil and low rainfall.

Describe **two** adaptations which plants growing in these areas will have to help them survive.

1 _____

2 _____   2

[Turn over

Marks

7. An experiment was set up to study the response of woodlice to light. Ten woodlice were placed in a glass tube. After five minutes one end of the tube was covered with black paper to make it dark. The number of woodlice in light and dark was then recorded every minute for five minutes.

The diagram below shows the apparatus used.

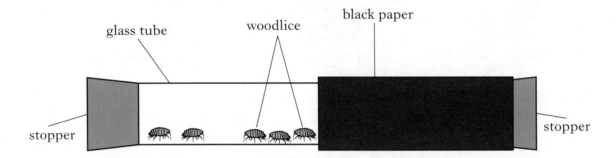

The table below shows the results of the experiment.

Time (minutes)	Number of woodlice	
	In light	In dark
0	5	5
1	6	4
2	4	6
3	3	7
4	2	8
5	1	9

(a) Why were the woodlice left for five minutes before the black paper was placed on the tube?

_____

_____   1

7. (continued)

Marks

(b) Complete the line graph on the grid below to show the number of woodlice found in the dark at each minute during the experiment.

The results for woodlice in light have already been plotted.

(Additional graph paper, if required, will be found on *Page twenty-eight*.)

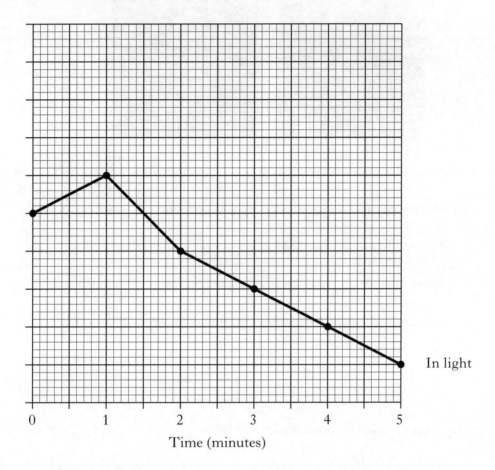

Time (minutes)

In light

2

(c) State a conclusion which can be drawn from the results of this experiment.

_____

_____ 1

(d) A student repeated this experiment.

   (i) How could the design be changed to make the results more reliable?

   _____

   _____ 1

   (ii) State one environmental factor which would be kept the same to allow a valid comparison with the first experiment.

   _____ 1

Marks

8.   Sorghum is an important food crop in some parts of the world.

The colour of the seed husk (coat) is controlled by a single gene.

Purple husk colour (H) is dominant to tan husk colour (h).

(*a*)   A true breeding purple husk plant is crossed with a true breeding tan husk plant.

(i)   What other term is used in genetics to indicate true breeding?

(**Circle**) the correct term below.

heterozygous   polygenic   homozygous   recessive   **1**

(ii)   Complete the genotypes of the parental (P) generation below:

P   purple   X   tan

P   genotypes   _____   _____   **1**

(iii)   State the phenotype(s) of the F$_1$ plants.

F$_1$ phenotype(s) _____   **1**

(*b*)   An individual from the F$_1$ generation is crossed with a true breeding tan husk plant.

(i)   Complete the Punnett square to show the expected results of this cross.

Genotypes of gametes
from F$_1$ plant

Genotype of gametes from tan husk plant		

2

(ii)   State the expected phenotype ratio for the offspring of this cross.

_____ : _____
purple   tan   **1**

Marks

9. (*a*) <u>Underline</u> **one** option in each set of brackets to make the following sentences correct.

Chromosomes are made of DNA. The chain of $\begin{Bmatrix} \text{acids} \\ \text{bases} \end{Bmatrix}$ in DNA

code for $\begin{Bmatrix} \text{amino acids} \\ \text{fatty acids} \end{Bmatrix}$ in $\begin{Bmatrix} \text{fats} \\ \text{proteins} \end{Bmatrix}$.

2

(*b*) Match each human cell with its possible chromosome complements by connecting them with a line.

Each human cell may be connected to more than one chromosome complement.

Human cell		*Chromosome complement*
white blood cell		22 + X
female gamete		22 + Y
male gamete		44 + XX

2

[Turn over

Marks

10. The following diagram shows the human heart.

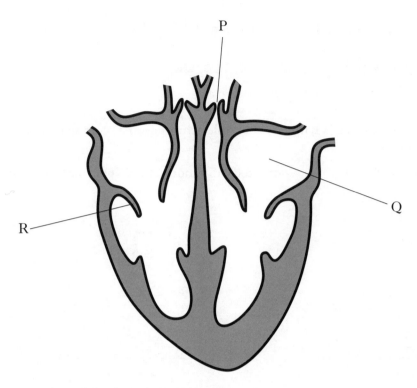

(*a*) (i) Name chamber Q and valve R.

Q _____   1

R _____   1

(ii) Describe the function of valve P.

_____

_____

_____   2

(iii) **Add** an arrow **to the diagram** showing where blood enters the heart
from the lungs.   1

(*b*) Name the blood vessel that carries blood to the lungs.

_____   1

Marks

11. (*a*) The diagram below shows the human digestive system.

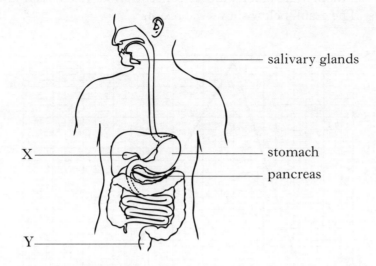

   (i) Name structures X and Y.

   X _____

   Y _____   **1**

   (ii) Draw lines to link each structure with the enzyme(s) that it produces.
   Each structure may be linked to more than one enzyme.

Structure	*Enzyme*
Salivary glands	Amylase
Stomach	Lipase
Pancreas	Pepsin

   2

(*b*) Glucose is absorbed from the small intestine into blood capillaries in the villi before being transported to the liver.

   (i) State **one** feature of a villus that increases the rate of absorption of glucose.

   _____   **1**

   (ii) Name the blood vessel that transports glucose from the small intestine to the liver.

   _____   **1**

   (iii) Excess glucose is stored in the liver. Name the storage carbohydrate found in the liver.

   _____   **1**

Marks

12. A person's blood glucose concentration was measured. The person then drank a glass of 25% glucose solution. The blood glucose concentration was measured over the next 150 minutes. The graph below shows the results.

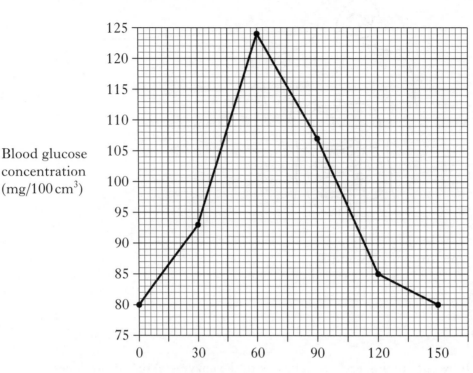

Blood glucose concentration (mg/100 cm³)

Time after drinking the glucose solution (minutes)

(a) **Use data from the graph** to describe the changes in blood glucose concentration over this 150 minute period.

_____

_____

_____ 2

(b) Calculate the percentage increase in blood glucose concentration from 0 to 60 minutes.

Space for calculation

_____ % 1

(c) It was predicted that drinking a glass of 10% glucose solution would give a lower blood glucose concentration after 60 minutes. When this test was carried out, the result was the same as shown on the graph.

Give **one** possible source of error that caused this result.

_____

_____ 1

Marks

13. The diagram below represents a section of human skin. Skin is involved in temperature regulation. Sweating is one response made by the skin to regulate body temperature.

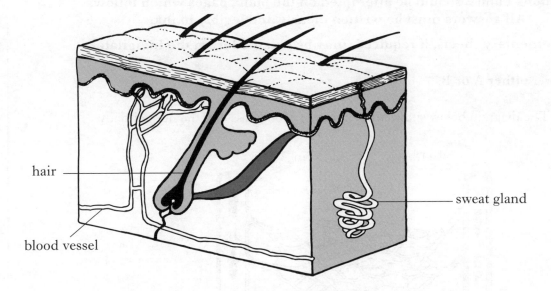

hair

blood vessel

sweat gland

(a) A **decrease** in body temperature leads to a response by the skin blood vessels.

(i) State the response of the skin blood vessels.

_____   1

(ii) Explain how this response helps to regulate body temperature.

_____

_____   1

(b) Underline **one** option in each set of brackets to make the sentence correct.

An increase in blood temperature is detected in the $\left\{\begin{array}{l}\text{hypothalamus}\\\text{medulla}\end{array}\right\}$ and then

$\left\{\begin{array}{l}\text{hormone}\\\text{nerve}\end{array}\right\}$ messages are sent to the sweat glands to $\left\{\begin{array}{l}\text{decrease}\\\text{increase}\end{array}\right\}$ sweating.   2

[Turn over for Section C on *Page twenty-four*

SECTION C

Marks

Both questions in this section should be attempted.

Note that each question contains a choice.

Questions 1 and 2 should be attempted on the blank pages which follow. All answers must be written clearly and legibly in ink.

Supplementary sheets, if required, may be obtained from the Invigilator.

1. Answer **either** A **or** B.

   A.   The diagram below shows three types of blood vessel in the human body.

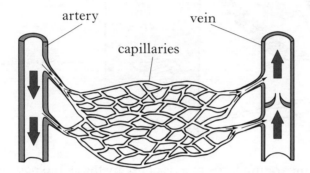

   For each of the three types of blood vessel shown, describe their

   (*a*)   structure;

   (*b*)   function.   5

   OR

   B.   The diagram below shows how negative feedback is used to control the water concentration of blood in the human body.

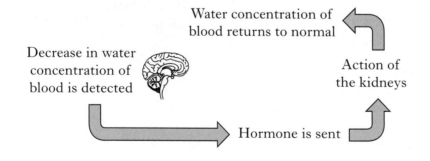

   Describe how the following organs respond to a **decrease** in the water concentration of the blood:

   (*a*)   the brain;

   (*b*)   the kidney.   5

Question 2 is on *Page twenty-six*

Marks

SPACE FOR ANSWER TO QUESTION 1

[Turn over for Question 2 on *Page twenty-six*

Marks

2. Answer **either** A **or** B.

   Labelled diagrams may be included where appropriate.

   A. Explain why numbers of the **light form** of peppered moth (*Biston betularia*) changed over a number of generations when air pollution in their environment was reduced.　**5**

   OR

   B. Bacteria can be used in genetic engineering. Describe the stages involved in this process. State **one** advantage and **one** disadvantage of genetic engineering.　**5**

[END OF QUESTION PAPER]

DO NOT
WRITE
IN THIS
MARGIN

SPACE FOR ANSWER TO QUESTION 2

ADDITIONAL SPACE FOR ANSWERS

ADDITIONAL GRAPH PAPER FOR QUESTION 7(*b*)

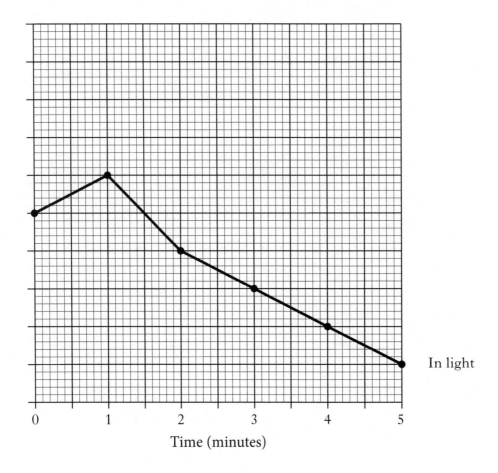

Time (minutes)

DO NOT
WRITE
IN THIS
MARGIN

ADDITIONAL SPACE FOR ANSWERS

Acknowledgements

Permission has been sought from all relevant copyright holders and Hodder Gibson is grateful for the use of the following:
Image © Gualberto Becerra/Shutterstock.com (2013 page 18);
Image © Joney/Shutterstock.com (2013 page 18).

INTERMEDIATE 2 | ANSWER SECTION

BIOLOGY INTERMEDIATE 2
2009

SECTION A

1. A	11. C	21. C
2. A	12. B	22. A
3. C	13. D	23. B
4. A	14. C	24. D
5. A	15. C	25. D
6. C	16. D	
7. B	17. C	
8. D	18. B	
9. B	19. A	
10. D	20. D	

SECTION B

1. (a) (i) YZX
   (ii) 3

   (b) protein

   (c) (The active site/enzyme/it) is altered/changes
   shape/structure becomes deformed **or**
   No longer specific/fits its substrate **or**
   Stops working/becomes inactive

2. (a) (pH) 9

   (b) pH

   (c) Makes the results more reliable
   To minimise unusual/atypical results

   (d)

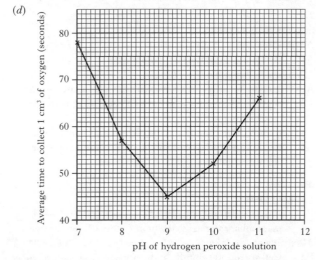

   (e) 67 - 87

3. (a) aerobic

   (b) (i) X = pyruvic acid/pyruvate
   Y = ATP

   (ii) Oxygen

   (c) (i) Anaerobic/fermentation

   (ii) produces alcohol/ethanol

4. (a) (i) 5%

   (ii) Only ATP causes muscle/tissue to contract

   (b) (i) (muscle) fatigue

   (ii) it is changed back into pyruvic acid **or**
   repay oxygen debt **or**
   more oxygen to tissue/muscle/it

5. (a) (i) Herbivore/(primary) consumer

   (ii)

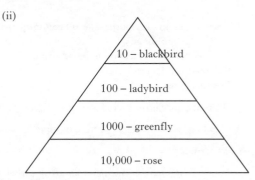

   (iii) Used in/lost as heat/in movement/in waste /indigestible
   material/lost as waste product
   or correct example

   (b) They belong to the same/one species

6. (a) 11 : 1

   (b) discontinuous

   (c) (i) A and B

   (ii) Both alleles are expressed equally in the phenotype **or**
   Both are equal/dominant to each other **or**
   Both in the phenotype

7. (a) (i) Zygote/fertilised (egg) cell

   (ii) Q

   (iii) **Double set** anther, R, embryo

   Single set ovule

   (b) Double set (of chromosomes) is restored when the zygote is
   formed/to restore chromosome number at fertilisation **or**
   So offspring have a set (of chromosomes) from each parent
   or
   To allow two single sets to join in the zygote/ embryo at
   fertilisation

   (c) Meiosis increases variation

8. (a) Temperature **or**
   humidity/moisture/damp

   (b) Woodlice spend most time in dark/least time in light/(most)
   woodlice move into the dark/out of the light

   (c) Protects/Prevents them drying out
   or escapes/hidden from predators
   or increases chances of survival

9. (a) (i) Variation/difference in size and shape
   or
   Length and width/depth/height

   (ii) (Availability of different types of)
   food/habitat/diet/prey/competition for food/habitat

(b) Niche

(c) (i) Deforestation/destruction of habitat/hunting/trapping/pollution/introduction of non-native species/tourism/forestry/farming

(ii) Decrease (due to extinction/dying out of species)

10. (a) (i) D C A B

(ii) A or B

(b)　　　　false　　high

true

　　　　false　　increases

11. (a) (i) B

(ii) Less protein in diet/more water intake/dilute urine/low ADH/toxic/poisonous
High Water Concentration in blood/urine
Kidney/liver damage/disease
Less deamination

(iii) (Litmus paper turns blue) more quickly/shorter times

(iv) (distilled) water in place of urine (sample)

(b) (i) glomerulus

(ii) Water/salts/glucose/some materials are absorbed into the blood /reabsorbed/absorbed from the filtrate

12. (a) D
bronchus/bronchi
air-sac/alveoli
A

(b) (i) 15

(ii) 3

13. (a) (i) Brain and spinal cord

(ii) Medulla

(b) (i) Sensory neurone/nerve **or** receptor

(ii) Pass nerve impulse/message/information (from sensory neurone) to motor neurone

(c) Reduces harm to the body/to move away from harmful stimuli **or**
Protect from danger/damage/harm **or**
Rapid/automatic/involuntary response to avoid harm/protect

SECTION C

1A

Maximum of three from:
P1　Chlorophyll/chloroplasts absorbs (energy of) light
P2　to split water into hydrogen and oxygen
P3　oxygen released
P4　ATP produced
P5　Light energy converted to chemical energy
P6　Hydrogen combines with a hydrogen acceptor
Maximum of three from:
C1　Carbon dioxide enters
C2　This stage is enzyme controlled
C3　ATP supplies the energy needed
C4　Hydrogen joins with Carbon dioxide
C5　Glucose/starch/cellulose is formed.

1B

Maximum of three from:
A1　Surrounding/Hypotonic solution has higher water concentration
A2　Water enters/fills (animal) cells/water diffuses into cells
A3　By osmosis/from HWC to LWC (or P3)
A4　Cells swell
A5　And burst
A6　Because no cell wall present
Maximum of three from:
P1　Surrounding/Hypertonic solution has lower water concentration
P2　Water leaves (plant) cells/water diffuses out of cells
P3　By osmosis/from HWC to LWC (or A3)
P4　Vacuole shrinks
P5　Cell membrane pulled away from cell wall/cell contents shrink
P6　Cell becomes plasmolysed/flaccid

2A

Maximum of three from:
Digestion
D1　Liver manufactures bile
D2　Bile emulsifies fats/forms smaller fat droplets/neutralises stomach contents/acids
D3　Pancreas produces digestive enzymes **or** named enzyme
Named enzyme plus substrate or product e.g.
D4　amylase breaks down starch
D5　lipase produces fatty acids and glycerol
D6　trypsin breaks down proteins/peptides

Maximum of three from:
Processing
P1　Glucose used in production of energy/ATP/respiration
P2　Glucose converted to glycogen in liver **or**
Vitamins/minerals stored in the liver
P3　Amino acids used in growth/repair/protein formation
P4　Excess amino acids deaminated in liver
P5　To form urea

2B

Maximum of one from:
Antibodies
A1　antibodies produced by lymphocytes
Maximum of two from:
A2　specific to antigen/bacteria/virus/foreign material/microbes
A3　combines/joins/fits with antigen/bacteria/virus/foreign material/microbes
A4　bacteria/virus/foreign material/microbes contain antigens
A5　destroys bacteria/virus/foreign material/microbes **or** agglutination

Maximum of one from:
Phagocytosis
P1　Phagocytosis carried out by macrophages/phagocytes/monocytes
Maximum of two from:
P2　Cell surrounds/engulfs antigen/bacteria/virus/foreign material/microbes
P3　Into a vesicle/vacuole
P4　Cell digests antigen/bacteria/virus/foreign material/microbes
P5　Using enzymes

BIOLOGY INTERMEDIATE 2
2010

SECTION A

1. B	11. B	21. D
2. A	12. D	22. B
3. C	13. B	23. C
4. B	14. C	24. A
5. D	15. A	25. D
6. B	16. C	
7. A	17. A	
8. D	18. C	
9. C	19. B	
10. A	20. D	

SECTION B

1. (a) (i) Controls entry and exit of materials
Contains genetic information **or** controls cell activities (specific activity must be correct) Cytoplasm

   (ii) **Q and**
   contains cell wall/vacuole

   (b) (i) bacteria
   lactose

   (ii) Alcohol **and** petrol

   (iii) To kill/destroy <u>bacteria</u> **or** prevent <u>bacterial</u> growth

2. (a) (i) Oxygen

   (ii) Water

   (iii) Add boiled liver instead

   (iv) Measure volume/height of foam (in a given time)

   (b) *Any two from:*
   Concentration of hydrogen peroxide
   Time left for
   pH
   Temperature of enzyme/tissue

   (c) Active site/enzyme shape changes **or** substrate no longer fits

3. (a) 38

   (b) Y → X

   (c) **Name**   Glycolysis
   Product   Pyruvic acid

4. (a) X   light intensity
   Y   carbon dioxide concentration

   (b) Number of bubbles/volume of oxygen produced per unit time
   or CO2 uptake with time
   or increase in dry mass with time

   (c) (i) Chlorophyll/chloroplast

   (ii) Used to split water **or** to form ATP **or** converted to <u>chemical</u> energy

   (d) (i) Carbon fixation

   (ii) Glucose

5. (a) More squid/food available for seals (to eat) or
   Less competition for food

(b)

Statement	True	False	Correction
In this food web krill are <u>herbivores</u>		✓	Omnivores
The population of <u>sperm whales</u> has the highest biomass		✓	Plant plankton
The range of species in a <u>population</u> is called biodiversity		✓	Community/ Ecosystem/ habitat

6. (a) (i) WW (both caps/same size

   (ii) Male gametes R, W (any order)
   Offspring RW, RR (RW, RR)

   (b) Polygenic

   (c) Blood group – discontinous **and**
   Height – continuous

   (d) The effect of the environment on phenotype/ appearance

7. (a) 69

   (b) Very low

   (c) x-axis scale and label correct
   y-axis scale correct
   Three bars for **average times** plotted accurately
   <u>both</u> axes must use at least 50% of graph paper provided

   (d) As light intensity increases, time taken to travel 10cm decreases **or** vice versa

8. (a) (i) Prey **and** secondary

   (ii) 64 (%)

   (b) No effect **and** no <u>species</u> becomes extinct
   or
   Decrease **and** <u>species</u> become extinct/number of species decreases

   (c) Sewage/fertilizers/industry/oil/acid rain

9. (a) P (salivary) amylase
   Q pepsin

   (b) Muscles behind food contract **and** in front of food relax (1)
   Food is pushed (down the small intestine) (1)

   (c) *Any two from:*
   Increased surface area/villi/long/folded (1)
   Thin (gut) wall/lining (1)
   Good blood supply (1)

10. (a) (i) P arrow towards lungs **and**
    Q arrow towards the body

    (ii) P deoxygenated **and**
    Q oxygenated

    (b) S <u>left</u> atrium
    R pulmonary <u>vein</u>

    (c) To stop backflow <u>of blood</u>

    (d) Reduces blood (flow)/glucose/oxygen to heart muscle

11. (a) Y   filtration   more

    (b) Liver

    (c) Osmoregulation

12. (a) Alcohol increases (average) reaction <u>times</u>

(b) To reduce effect of rogue <u>results</u>/to improve reliability of <u>results</u>

(c) 50 (%)

(d) Cerebellum

SECTION C

1A
Maximum of two from:
L1   Air/oxygen breathed in through trachea/windpipe/ nose/mouth
L2   Air/oxygen passes down through bronchi/ bronchioles
L3   Air/oxygen moves into alveolus/air sac
L4   Oxygen <u>dissolves/diffuses</u> through (moist) lining/wall

Maximum of two from:
B1   Into red blood cell
B2   Into capillary/blood/forms oxygenated blood
B3   Joins to haemoglobin/forms oxyhaemoglobin
B4   Blood taken to heart (via pulmonary vein)

Maximum of two from:
S1   From heart via aorta/arteries
S2   Carried <u>to skin</u> (cells)
S3   Oxyhaemoglobin gives up oxygen to (skin) cells/oxygen passes into cells

D   Higher oxygen concentration to lower oxygen concentration (can be awarded only once in section L **or** S)

1B
Maximum of two from:
C1   Act as energy store
C2   Provide energy (via respiration)
C3   Contain C, H and O (or full names)
C4   Simple sugars/glucose

Maximum of two from:
F1   Insulation energy store/provides energy
F2   Contain C, H and O
F3   Fatty acids
F4   Glycerol

Maximum of two from:
P1   Growth/repair
P2   Contain C, H, O and N
P3   Amino acids

2A
Maximum of three from:
Adaptions
A1   Roots − long/deep
A2   Superficial/shallow/under surface roots
A3   Small leaves/no leaves/spines/needles/thorns/spikes
A4   <u>Thick waxy cuticle</u> (on leaves) (not skin)
A5   Succulent tissue/any other correct desert adaptation

Maximum of three from:
Explanations − must relate to the correct point above
E1   (Increases chance of) <u>absorbing</u> water from <u>deep</u> soil (for A1)
E2   (Increases chance of) <u>absorbing surface</u> water (for A2)
E3   Decreases/reduces water loss (for A3 or A4)
E4   Protects plant from animals (for A3)
E5   Stores water (for A5)/any other correct explanation to match A5

2B
Maximum of three from:
Differences body cells and gametes
D1   Zygote/body <u>cells</u> (or named examples) have double sets/diploid/pairs of chromosomes
D2   Gametes have single set/haploid/half the parent cell chromosome number
D3   Zygote/body <u>cells</u> have 46/23 pairs of chromosomes
D4   Gametes have 23 chromosomes

Maximum of three from:
Sex determination
S1   Male gametes/sperm contain X or Y chromosome
S2   Female gametes/eggs contain an X chromosome
S3   At fertilisation the zygote is formed
    or at fertilisation the gametes fuse
S4   XX − Female (human) **or** XY − Male (human)
S5   Sperm/male gamete determine the sex of (human) offspring

BIOLOGY INTERMEDIATE 2
2011

SECTION A

1. D	**11.** B	**21.** C
2. B	**12.** C	**22.** D
3. C	**13.** A	**23.** A
4. D	**14.** A	**24.** B
5. A	**15.** C	**25.** A
6. D	**16.** C	
7. B	**17.** A	
8. C	**18.** D	
9. B	**19.** B	
10. D	**20.** B	

SECTION B

1. (*a*) (i) X = (sap) vacuole
           Y = cytoplasm

     (ii) stores genetic information/DNA/chromosomes
           controls cell activity(ies)/function(s)

   (*b*) (potato/starch) phosphorylase

   (*c*) D = only plants have a cell wall/chloroplast/vacuole
         S = both have membranes/cytoplasm/nuclei

2. (*a*) fungi   carbon dioxide   gasohol

   (*b*) (bacteria) convert <u>lactose to lactic acid</u>
         lactic acid clots milk/causes curdling

3. (*a*) (i) X and Y axes labels and units correct (as table)
         (ii) Correct plot and join of all points

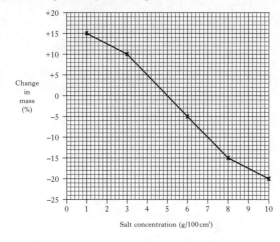

   (*b*) *Any two from:*
         type/size/number of potato/cylinders
         type/pH/volume of (salt) <u>solution</u>
         temperature

   (*c*) 5 [or where graph line crosses X axis]
         no change in <u>mass/weight</u>

   (*d*) 7 [or correct value from graph]

4. (*a*) enzyme has an active site

         enzyme/active site is complementary/matching
         shape/specific to substrate

   (*b*) denatured/
         changes <u>shape</u>/
         reduced activity

   (*c*) pH **or** concentration of enzyme/substrate

   (*d*) water and oxygen

5. (*a*) habitat/holt

   (*b*) less shelter/place to live/habitat/breeding ground/food
         available
         (more chance of being) seen by predators/prey
         increased competition for habitat

   (*c*) otter numbers would decrease
         (otters and mink) in competition for food/fish/habitat

   (*d*) producer

                    eats animals <u>only</u>

                    <u>all</u> the plants and animals/
                    populations/
                    species/
                    organisms/
                    living things

6. (*a*) 320

   (*b*) 50% (increase) / 33% / 33.3% (decrease)

   (*c*) (i) (pheno) type/variety of cotton/
             plant resistant or not

         (ii) to compare mass/yields/
              to show any difference in mass/yields is due to variety
              of cotton

         (iii) improve/increase reliability of <u>results</u>

   (*d*) R cotton produces a higher yield (than V cotton)

   (*e*) (i) It is resistant to the boll weevil/insects

         (ii) Less pesticide so fewer insects die

7. (*a*) (i) HH, hh
         (ii) Wavy
         (iii) Hh

   (*b*) co-dominant

   (*c*) order, bases, protein

8. (*a*) stomach and <u>small</u> intestine

   (*b*) (i) 2000
         (ii) 67/66·7

9. (*a*) it increases then decreases
         maximum/optimum/highest/change at <u>pH8</u>

   (*b*) depth of clear jelly will be less than 2 mm/any value less
         than 2mm

   (*c*) *Any two from:*
         lipase
         amylase
         peptidase

10. (*a*) hypotonic   excreting   concentrated

   (*b*) (i) Q = Bowman's capsule
         (ii) (ultra)filtration

   (*c*) (i) pituitary gland
         (ii) Tubule/collecting duct/loop of Henle

11. (*a*) True
         False   speed up
         False   carbon dioxide

   (*b*) (as) oxyhaemoglobin/(on) haemoglobin

(c) *Any two from:*

carbon dioxide/sugars/glucose/amino acids/
proteins/fats/vitamins/urea/hormones/salts/
water/oxygen/antibodies/platelets

12. (a) *Any three from:*

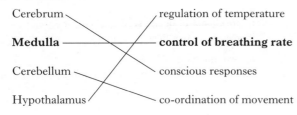

Cerebrum — regulation of temperature

Medulla —— **control of breathing rate**

Cerebellum — conscious responses

Hypothalamus — co-ordination of movement

(b) (i) 1. sensory
    2. relay/association/interneurone
    3. motor

(ii) provides a rapid response/
     protects the body (from harm)/
     prevent further damage

SECTION C

1A

N1   X is a pyramid of numbers

Maximum of two from:

N2   oak tree few/one
N3   caterpillar more numerous than oak
N4   any correct number relationship between hawk and thrush **or** caterpillar and thrush
N5   numbers decrease moving along the food chain (caterpillar to hawk)
N6   any correct description of 'block' sizes

Maximum of two from:

E1   oak tree has highest energy
E2   correct position of any organism in the pyramid
E3   caterpillar/thrush/hawk level has less energy than any level below
E4   energy used/decreases/lost at each stage
E5   (energy lost by) movement/heat/waste products (or any other correct)
E6   any correct description of 'block' sizes

1B

M1   Cell A sperm/**male** gamete/**male** sex cell

Maximum of two from:

M2   (matching/homologous) chromosomes pair **or** random assortment
M3   produces variation
M4   double set/2 sets/diploid/46 chromosomes
M5   pairs separate
M6   gametes/sex cell 1 set/haploid/23/ half the number of chromosomes
M7   <u>four</u> gametes/sex cells produced

Maximum of two from:

F1   gametes/sex cells fuse
F2   any correct description of fusion of gamete/sex cell <u>nuclei</u> (*must indicate male/female*)
F3   to form a zygote
F4   this is a random process
F5   produces variation
F6   X sperm produce female offspring/Y sperm produce male offspring
F7   zygote contains/restores 2 sets/diploid/46 chromosomes

2A

Maximum of three from:

G1   overall equation [*not under stage 1*]
G2   **first stage** is glycolysis
G3   enzyme controlled
G4   glucose is broken down/used/raw material
G5   pyruvic acid is produced
G6   **2** ATP produced
G7   anaerobic stage/no oxygen needed

Maximum of three from:

K1   second stage enzyme controlled
K2   pyruvic acid used/raw material
K3   oxygen used/raw material
K4   <u>36</u> ATP produced/total <u>38</u> ATP produced
K5   carbon dioxide <u>and</u> water produced

2B

Maximum of three from:

P1   overall equation [including light and chlorophyll] [*not under stage 1*]
P2   **first stage** is photolysis/light reaction
P3   enzyme controlled
P4   light energy trapped by chlorophyll
P5   water is broken down/used/raw material
P6   oxygen is released/produced
P7   ATP/hydrogen is produced
P8   ATP/hydrogen is passed to second stage

Maximum of three from:

C1   **second stage** is carbon fixation/Calvin's cycle/light independent reaction
C2   enzyme controlled
C3   carbon dioxide is used/raw material
C4   ATP provides energy/hydrogen used
C5   hydrogen added to carbon dioxide
C6   glucose is produced

BIOLOGY INTERMEDIATE 2 2012

SECTION A

1. C	**11.** D	**21.** A
2. B	**12.** A	**22.** C
3. C	**13.** D	**23.** A
4. D	**14.** D	**24.** C
5. C	**15.** B	**25.** B
6. A	**16.** B	
7. C	**17.** D	
8. A	**18.** D	
9. B	**19.** B	
10. A	**20.** A	

SECTION B

1. (*a*) (i) lactic acid

  (ii) yoghurt

 (*b*) (i) yeast/fungus

  (ii) (alcohol) mixed with petrol/to form gasohol

2. (*a*) *Any two – only one from each line:*
   mass of substrate/enzyme
   volume of substrate/enzyme
   concentration of substrate/enzyme
   same substrate/enzyme
   temperature
   time left to run

 (*b*) (i) 8

  (ii) 5

3. (*a*) (i) glycolysis

  (ii) pyruvic acid

  (iii) oxygen

 (*b*) (i) stage 1 = 2
   stage 1 + 2 = 38

  (ii) ADP **and** Pi

  (iii) *Any one from:*
   muscle contraction/movement/synthesis (of
   proteins)/growth/cell division/transmission of nerve
   impulses/heat production

4. (*a*) selectively/semi permeable/has pores

 (*b*) B and D

 (*c*) (blotted) dry

 (*d*) B

   has the greatest difference in concentration/concentration
   gradient

5. (*a*) (i)

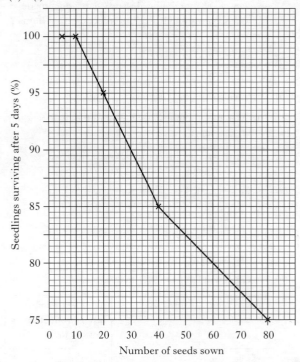

   correct scale on x-axis and correct scale on y-axis
   (more than 50% each axis used)

   correct plots and joined

  (ii) number of seeds

  (iii) the higher the <u>competition</u>, the lower the <u>% of
   seedlings</u> surviving

  (iv) 4:3

  (v) 55

 (*b*) *Any one from:*
   light/nutrients/space

6. (*a*) F prey
   F two
   T

 (*b*) (i) ⟶ water snails ⟶ stone loaches ⟶
   ⟶ brown trout ⟶ heron

  (ii) <u>energy</u> flow

 (*c*) energy lost as it passes through the food chain

   heron has least energy available to build tissues
   or
   fewer heron than any other organism
   (must be comparative)

7. (*a*) bacterial cell E
   insulin gene C
   plasmid   D

 (*b*) plasmid replicated
   or
   bacteria/cell multiplied

 (*c*) growth hormone

 (*d*) increased range of <u>products</u>/increased rate of
   <u>production/produced quicker</u>
   large/increased volume/mass of <u>product</u> (or named
   example)/
   lower cost of <u>production</u>/
   less/no allergy to <u>product</u>

or

an example of moral/ethical issue e.g. <u>product</u> made without killing animals/without infection from human donors

8. (*a*) Cell 1   Cell 3

(*b*) (i) meiosis

(ii) Matching/homologous chromosomes pair/random assortment

pairs separate into different cells/single sets/chromosome number halved

(*c*) zygote   nuclei   fuse

9. (*a*) (i) lymphocyte

(ii) red blood cells/haemoglobin

(iii) oxyhaemoglobin

(*b*) % oxygen will fall from 91% to 80%/by 11%

less oxygen	causes/so	more lactic acid/ faster production of lactic acid
less aerobic		less muscle contraction
anaerobic		less energy

Answer to include one from each column

10. (*a*) 6

(*b*) (i) 75

(ii) 126

(*c*) used <u>twenty</u> students

11. (*a*) A   trachea/windpipe
B   bronchus/bronchi
C   bronchioles

(*b*) (i) diffusion

(ii) *Any two from:*

thin walled/large surface area/numerous/

moist (lining)/good blood supply/in close contact with capillaries

12. (*a*)

	Q	
association/relay/ inter/connecting neurone		
	S	contracts/moves/ brings about response

(*b*) medulla   cerebellum   hypothalamus

(*c*) ADH

SECTION C

1A

N1   any correct named enzyme and substrate

Maximum of two from:

E1   enzyme has active site

E2   enzyme lowers energy input/speeds up chemical reactions

E3   <u>active site</u> is specific/complementary fit/lock and key/ enzyme-substrate complex

E4   enzyme unchanged at end/can be reused

Maximum of two from:

S1   substrate broken down into smaller/more soluble molecules

S2   named products (must match with N1)

S3   products released from enzyme/active site

1B

Maximum of three from:

P1   <u>light from lamp</u> absorbed by *Elodea*/plant/ chlorophyll/chloroplast

P2   energy used to split water

P3   into H and O

P4   energy used to produce ATP

Maximum of three from:

C1 CO_2 <u>in water</u> joins with H

C2   using ATP

C3   to form glucose

C4   glucose molecules joined to produce starch

C5   enzyme controlled

2A

Maximum of two from:

M1   muscles contract and relax

M2   mix/churn <u>food</u> with gastric juices/enzymes/acid/pepsin

M3   physical breakdown of food/smaller pieces/bigger surface area

Maximum of two from:

CA1   hydrocholoric acid/HCl

CA2   optimum pH for pepsin/enzyme activity

CA3   pepsin/enzyme digest protein

CA4   acid activates pepsin (ogen)

Maximum of two from:

CM1   mucus coats/lines stomach wall

CM2   to prevent/protect from damage/digestion by acid/enzyme

2B

Maximum of two from:

B1   hypothalamus/brain detects rise in <u>blood</u> temperature

B2   hypothalamus receives nerve impulses from skin/thermo receptors

or hypothalamus sends nerve impulses to skin

B3   negative feedback

B4   any voluntary response to reduce body temperature

Maximum of three from:

S1   increased sweating/sweat glands stimulated

S2   increases heat loss by evaporation

S3   blood vessels/arterioles dilate/vasodilation

S4   increasing blood flow to skin

S5   increasing heat loss by radiation

S6   hairs lie flat so less air trapped

BIOLOGY INTERMEDIATE 2
2013

SECTION A

1. B	11. D	21. C
2. A	12. A	22. D
3. B	13. A	23. C
4. D	14. D	24. A
5. D	15. C	25. B
6. C	16. B	
7. B	17. C	
8. B	18. C	
9. D	19. A	
10. A	20. D	

SECTION B

1. (a) photosynthesis/makes food
traps/absorbs/takes in light
contains chlorophyll

   vacuole controls/allows/entry and exit (of materials)

   (b) (i) vacuole/cytoplasm shrunken Membrane/cytoplasm pulled away from wall
   (ii) no net <u>water</u> movement/equal <u>water/osmosis</u> in and out

   equal (water/salt) <u>concentration</u> inside and out/ no <u>concentration</u> gradient

2. (a) X

   bacteria continued to grow up to disc/no clear zone
bacteria unaffected

   (b) repeated use/overuse of antibiotics
   (c) fungi

3. (a) activity increased then decreased

   (b) 50

   (c) 40

   (d) activity is the same at each temperature/not affected by temperature

   (e) <4
   <u>enzyme/catalase</u> has been denatured;
   or <u>enzyme/ active site</u> has changed shape
   or temperature too high for activity

4. (a) (i) diffusion
   (ii) too large to fit/pass through the pores
   (iii) increase + <u>water</u> moves in

   water moves from high <u>water</u> concentration to low/water moves by osmosis/diffusion

   (b)
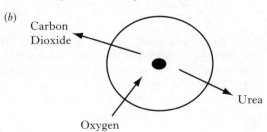

5. (a) carbon dioxide
green plants
cellulose

   (b) False/photolysis/light stage/reaction

   True

   False   ATP

6. (a) beak shapes/sizes/structures
different food sources/types

   (b) *Any two from:*
waxy cuticles/leaves
no/small leaves/spines/spikes
succulent tissues/fleshy stem
widespread roots

7. (a) to allow them to adjust/acclimatise to the conditions

   (b)
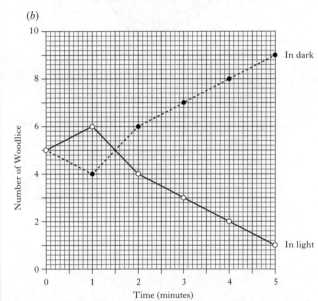

   correct scale and label on y-axis
correct plots joined and labelled 'in dark'

   (c) woodlice move towards dark/move away from light

   (d) (i) use more woodlice/repeat experiment again

   (ii) temperature/humidity/moisture/damp/light/dark (intensity)

8. (a) (i) homozygous

   (ii) HH   hh

   (iii) purple

   (b) (i)

	H	h
h	Hh	hh
h	Hh	hh

   both parental genotypes
correct offspring genotypes

   (ii) 1:1

9. (a) bases   amino acids   proteins

   (b) **Human cell   chromosome complement**

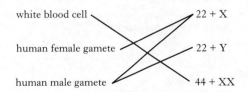

10. (*a*) (i) Q   left atrium

          R   tricuspid (valve)

             OR <u>right</u> atrio-ventricular/(valve)

    (ii) stop backflow of <u>blood</u>/so blood only flows in one direction

          into the heart/ventricle **or** from aorta

    (iii)

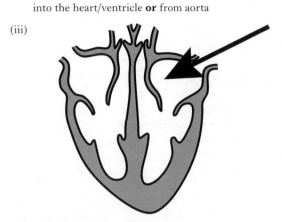

  (*b*) Pulmonary artery

11. (*a*) (i) X = Gall bladder

           Y = Rectum/large intestine/colon

    (ii)

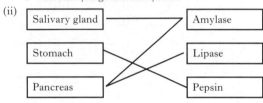

  (*b*) (i) *Any one from:*

          large surface area/capillary network/good blood supply

          thin lining/wall

    (ii) Hepatic portal vein

    (iii) Glycogen

12. (*a*) increases, then decreases/returns to start value

      three blood glucose concentrations: 80, 124, 80 (mg/100cm³) and at correct times

  (*b*) 55

  (*c*) *Any one from:*

      different volume/mass/wrong concentration of solution

      food or drink prior to test/exercise during test/different person

13. (*a*) (i) constriction/vasoconstriction/become narrower

    (ii) reduces blood flow to skin/less heat lost/more heat retained

  (*b*) hypothalamus; nerve; increase

SECTION C

1A (*a*)

Maximum of one from:

SA1   Thick muscular wall

SA2   Narrow/small/thin lumen/space/cavity

Maximum of one from:

SV1   Thin, muscular wall

SV2   Wide/large lumen/ space/cavity

SV3   Valves

Maximum of one from:

SC1   Walls one cell thick

SC2   Large surface area/network

1A (*b*)

Maximum of one from:

FA1   Carry <u>blood</u> at high pressure

FA2   Away from heart

Maximum of one from:

FV1   Carry <u>blood</u> at low pressure

FV2   Towards heart

Maximum of one from:

FC1   Link arteries and veins

FC2   Exchange of materials

1B (*a*)

Maximum of three from:

B1   One correct name from osmoreceptor/hypothalamus/pituitary gland

B2   Osmoreceptors/hypothalamus detect water concentration

B3   Hypothalamus sends messages to the pituitary gland

B4   Pituitary gland releases hormone

B5   ADH

B6   Hormone travels in blood

1B (*b*)

Maximum of three from:

K1   Increased/more ADH

K2   Increases permeability of (kidney) tubules/collecting ducts

K3   More <u>water</u> reabsorbed/ more <u>water</u> absorbed into <u>blood</u>

K4   less <u>urine</u> produced

K5   more concentrated <u>urine</u> produced

2A

Maximum of five from:

1. Two forms/description
2. Lighter bark/less soot
3. More lichen
4. Light form better camouflaged/ blend in/hidden
5. So less easily seen by predators
6. Fewer eaten/less predation
7. More survive to breed/ reproduce
8. Pass on characteristics/ genes
9. Numbers of light form increase

2B

Maximum of three from:

S1   Required gene identified/ located

S2   Enzymes used

S3   <u>Gene</u> removed from <u>chromosome</u>

S4   Plasmid removed from bacterial cell

S5   Plasmid cut open

S6   Gene inserted into plasmid/vector

S7   Plasmid inserted into (new) bacterial/host cell

S8   Bacterial cells grown/ cultured/multiply

S9   Insulin/ required product extracted/ purified/made

AND

G1   Increased range of products/

      Increased rate of production/increased volume of production/any other correct advantage

AND

G2   High cost of development/

      Possible release of genetically modified organisms into environment/transfer of antibiotic resistance/any other correct disadvantage